WILDFLOWER
GENETICS

A Field Guide for British Columbia and the Pacific Northwest

Anthony J.F. Griffiths
Fred R. Ganders

The University of British Columbia

flight press

ISBN 0-919843-00-**X**

Canadian Cataloging in Publication Data
Griffiths, Anthony J.F.
Wildflower genetics
Bibliography: p.
Includes index.
ISBN 0-919843-00-X
1. Wild flowers - British Columbia -
Identification. 2. Plant genetics.
I. Ganders, Fred R., 1945-   II. Title.
QK203.B7G75   582.13'09711   C83-091024-7

Designed by: Crystal Ryan
Typeset by: Empress Printing Inc.

Printed in Canada by Friesen Printers

Flight Press   3630 West Broadway, No. 2,
Vancouver, B.C., Canada V6R 2B7

WILDFLOWER
GENETICS

To Rachel, Maia, Claire, and Elaine
To H.K. and M.

CONTENTS

PREFACE

The goal of this book is to heighten your enjoyment and awareness of nature through a knowledge of genetics. Anyone who enjoys observing nature, especially plants, will derive even more pleasure from a greater understanding of genetics. Genetics provides a new way of looking at nature that offers insights into the complexities of the natural world.

Although observing, photographing, and identifying wildflowers, trees, and ferns is enjoyable in itself, it can be just a first step; the genetic viewpoint leads to further levels of involvement. At the first level, genetics can show you new ways of observing plants—new things to look for during your forays into nature. In this way, every walk along the seashore, in the forest, or through an alpine meadow can become a genetics field trip. You can even find examples of genetic variation in wildflowers along the highway or in an abandoned lot. The only skills you need are careful observation (often on all fours) and the ability to identify a plant.

The second level of involvement, which we hope will be stimulated in some readers, is simple experimentation. The way geneticists experiment is mainly by making crosses. It takes little skill to know how to make a cross, how to collect seeds, or how to count progeny types. Using these simple techniques, you can determine the causes of genetic variation in the plants you see on your hikes.

The aims of this book, then, are to foster the enjoyment of nature through genetics at two levels:

1. Observing genetic phenomena in plant populations.
2. Performing simple genetic experiments.

To help you achieve these aims, the book begins with a brief introduction to basic genetic principles. The subsequent chapters describe the different types of genetic variation found in plants, giving examples that we have observed in British Columbia. Although most of the examples are wildflowers, we have included some trees and ferns. You may wish to look for these examples, or you may prefer to find your own.

Although all the examples in this book are from British Columbia, two things must be made clear. First, although we have illustrated a fairly representative selection of the kinds of variation found in plants, this book is by no means complete. Many other interesting genetic examples occur, and many remain to be discovered. However, in most cases you should be able to find similar or analogous examples in the book that will help interpret what you have seen.

Second, although this book is a field guide to wildflower genetics in British Columbia, it is not really that provincial in its application. All of the plants illustrated occur outside the Province of British Columbia as well; many are widespread in western North America, and some occur throughout much of the Northern Hemisphere. So the examples we have illustrated are likely to be found in many places. In addition, all of the types of genetic variation illustrated are of general importance and occur in plants everywhere. Similar examples of mutations, polymorphisms, or hybrids can be found in different species in any geographic region; the same principles apply.

At the end of the book you will find information about where to look for genetic variation in wildflowers in British Columbia. A list of suggested readings tells you where to find out more about plant identification and genetics, and a glossary defines botanical and genetics terms you may not be familiar with.

Much of the research referred to in the book was funded by grants from the Canadian Natural Sciences and Engineering Research Council. In addition, special thanks are due to Al Rose, Horticulturalist of the BC Native Garden at the UBC Botanical Garden, who first showed us many of the examples described in the book. Ken Carey and Gerda Krause performed some of the experiments and assisted in the field work, and we are grateful for their help. We thank Dr. Kay Beamish for collecting the pink *Collinsia* mutant for us. Finally, we wish to thank Ila Westergard-Thorpe and Chris Poirier-Skelton for typing the several drafts of the manuscript.

The rewards of science are in the thrill of exploration and discovery. Many useful discoveries have been made by amateur students of nature, and we believe that many more remain to be made. These are well within the reach of the average person. Good luck in your explorations.

Anthony J.F. Griffiths
Fred R. Ganders

CHAPTER ONE

WHAT IS GENETICS?

Genetics is usually defined as the study of inheritance. Inheritance itself is the process of handing on, from one generation to the next, the characteristic traits that make up a living plant or animal. To be more precise, it is not the characteristics themselves that are handed down from parent to offspring but the instructions or blueprints for those characteristics. When we say, for example, "She has her mother's hair," what we really mean is "The instructions for growing hair like that were derived from her mother."

The "instructions" that we have just referred to are embodied in minute components of every cell called *genes*. The characteristics of a plant or animal are to a large degree dictated by the genes it bears. It is genes that make a dogwood tree a dogwood tree and not a red alder tree. Each gene has different forms, which are responsible for the many differences found within and between species. For example, the sea blush, *Plectritis congesta,* which grows on Vancouver Island and in the Gulf Island region of British Columbia, has two kinds of fruits. Wherever this species grows, some plants have fruits with wings and some have fruits with no wings (Figure 1.1). This difference is due to a difference in one kind of gene, which we could call the fruit-wing gene.

The existence of genes was discovered in the nine-

1

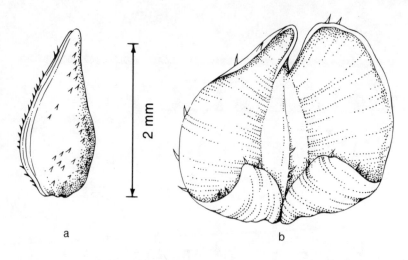

Figure 1.1   (*a*) Wingless and (*b*) winged fruit forms of the sea blush. Both forms, which occur on separate plants, are common in British Columbia. The difference is due to a single gene difference.

teenth century by Gregor Mendel, an Austrian monk, who performed experiments with the garden pea in a monastery garden about the size of the average Vancouver back yard. Since then genetics has grown into a highly sophisticated experimental discipline embracing chemistry, mathematics, and many areas of biology.

By and large genetics as a science can be divided into two major areas, transmission genetics and molecular genetics. *Transmission genetics* is concerned with pinpointing the existence of specific genes and following their patterns of transmission from one generation to the next. This book is concerned mainly with transmission genetics.

Molecular genetics is an exciting area of research whose goal is to understand the structure and function of genes at the molecular level. A great deal is now known about this subject, thanks to a large battery of sophisticated techniques, such as recombinant DNA technology. This knowledge can greatly enhance our understanding and appreciation of the way in which the hereditary blueprints in cells—

the genes—determine how a plant or animal looks and behaves. The color, shape, size, and other characteristics of an organism are under genetic control. The success of life on this planet is the success of the blueprints of life, the genes. Some biologists say that a plant or animal's body is simply a vehicle for serving the genes, existing only to protect them against environmental stress and to propagate them through time.

THE NATURE AND FUNCTION OF GENES

Organisms are simply large masses of cells. Figure 1.2 illustrates the components of a plant cell. A typical plant cell is surrounded by a *cell wall*. Inside, the cell is subdivided into two broad areas, the vacuole and the cytoplasm. The *vacuole* is a fluid-filled sac. The *cytoplasm* is the stuff of life and contains discrete organelles ("little organs") with specific functions. The most conspicuous are the *chloroplasts*, which contain the pigment chlorophyll. The job of chloroplasts is *photosynthesis*, in which light energy is used to convert carbon dioxide and water into sugar. Also present in the cytoplasm are smaller organelles called *mitochondria*, the energy factories of the cell.

In addition to these components, each cell has a *nucleus*, and in each nucleus there are rodlike structures called chromosomes (Figure 1.2). A *chromosome* is basically several centimeters of a threadlike chemical called DNA, which is very tightly coiled for convenient packaging. The DNA is divided into areas that are the genes. An analogy for a chromosome might be a meter stick (the total DNA of that chromosome) of which cm #1 is one kind of gene, cm #2 another kind of gene, and so on.

There are many types of chromosomes in a cell, and each cell of an organism has the same number of chromosomes. In higher plants and animals, each cell has two identical sets of each type of chromosome. Hence, each cell has two copies of

3

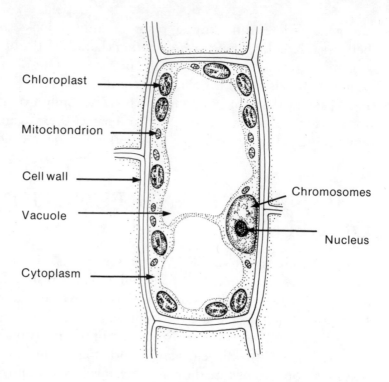

Chloroplast

Mitochondrion

Cell wall

Vacuole

Cytoplasm

Chromosomes

Nucleus

Figure 1.2   Generalized diagram of a plant cell, showing the major components.

every kind of gene, and these are called *gene pairs*. Figure 1.3 shows a cell with two sets of five chromosomes. A useful shorthand for describing this is $2n = 10$, $n = 5$, where n is the number of chromosomes in each chromosome set. In humans, $2n = 46$, or two sets of 23 unique chromosomes.

A gene can exist in several forms, called *alleles,* and it is the alleles that are responsible for variation within a species. For example, the gene for petal color in a flower might have an allele for red petals and an allele for white petals.

The alleles of a gene are represented by a letter. The *dominant* allele, or the one that "wins" when the two types of alleles are found together in an individual, is denoted by a capital letter. The *recessive* allele, or the one that "loses"

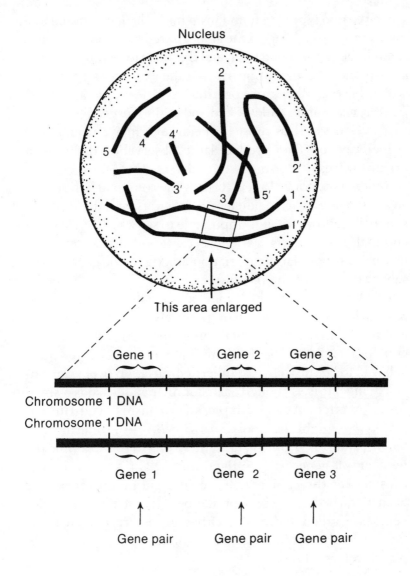

Figure 1.3   Diagrammatic illustration of the arrangement of genes on chromosomes. Each chromosome is a single coiled thread of DNA, which has been uncoiled for the purpose of this diagram. Note that the chromosomes and the genes occur in pairs.

when the two types are found in an individual, is denoted by a lower-case letter. Thus, if the allele for red petals is dominant, it might be represented by A, and the allele for white petals by a. A plant of constitution Aa is called a *heterozygote* and would be red. Plants of constitution AA and aa are called *homozygotes* and would be red and white, respectively.

Genes such as those for petal color may be thought of as major genes. They produce large, observable effects on an organism, resulting in discrete classes. One allele may be considered the normal allele (usually the dominant); the other, a variant allele. Variant alleles produce variant individuals. In some cases, however, it is impossible to say which allele is the "normal" and which is "variant" because both occur commonly in a natural population. Variation among major genes is the subject of most of the rest of the book.

Other genes, which may be considered minor genes, have a less striking effect by themselves. In fact, they are identified only through their cumulative effects in concert with other similar genes. This kind of gene is generally believed to be the source of inherited variation over a continuous range. It is as though each dominant allele adds a small "dose" of effect. As an example, an organism of constitution $b_1 b_1 b_2 b_2 b_3 b_3$ might be short; $b_1 b_1 B_2 B_2 B_3 B_3$, of intermediate height; and $B_1 B_1 B_2 B_2 B_3 B_3$, tall; and so on. (In this example the number of gene pairs influencing height was arbitrarily chosen to be three. Note that the different minor genes have been identified by a subscript number.) These types of minor genes are called *polygenes*. Other genes are known to be located in the cytoplasm, inside mitochondria and chloroplasts (refer to Figure 1.2).

How do genes work? The answer is simple: each gene contains the blueprints for making one specific kind of protein. Proteins are very important chemicals in cells. There are two major classes, structural proteins and catalytic proteins (*enzymes*). Examples of structural proteins in humans are found in hair, muscle, and skin, which are made largely of protein. It can be seen that different proteins have very different structural properties, and these determine the structural properties of the tissue, such as flexibility, strength, and fragility. Catalytic proteins have the crucial job of making chemical reactions in cells occur at speeds that are compatible with life as we know it. The cell is really a complex chemical factory with a myriad of reactions going on, mostly catalyzed by enzymes. So, by determining enzymes, genes have a sweeping control over the chemistry that is life.

Since all cells have the same set of genes, why are cells different? For example, the root hair of a celery plant is very different from the tough fiber cells in the celery stalk. The simple answer lies in the control of gene expression. In some cells one subset of genes is active, and in other cells a different subset of genes is active.

In summary, genes determine the uniqueness of a species, and variation in the allelic forms of genes from individual to individual in a population is responsible for hereditary variation. Thus we see that genetics explains both the constancy of a species and the variation within a species.

VARIATION: THE RAW MATERIAL OF GENETICS

The starting point of genetics is the observation of variation. If all the plants of one species in your walk are identical, you cannot begin a genetic discussion of them or perform genetic analysis on them. All geneticists, from Mendel to professional geneticists today, start their studies with members of a single species that differ with respect to at least one aspect of their makeup. For example, one member of a pair of foxgloves might have red petals and the other member white petals. Or one member of a pair of foxgloves might have smooth stems and the other member hairy stems.

The amateur interested in genetics must therefore find some variants. At first this can be discouraging; all members of a species tend to look remarkably uniform at first glance. There are two solutions to this problem: look more carefully, and look at more plants. You will probably have to get down on your hands and knees and hunt. If you are studying a large population of plants (this is easier with small plants), you can be almost certain of finding some variants. But even small populations may contain variants.

What kind of things can you look for? Figure 1.4 shows the various parts of a plant you may observe. Because the roots are below the ground it is difficult to observe them, but any part of the shoot is easily examined. Here are some general categories of traits that can be looked at.

1. *Color variation.* Usually this involves the flower petals—for example, blue versus white.
2. *Presence or absence of a structure*—for example, hairy versus smooth stems.
3. *Shape variation*—for example, round versus strap-like leaves.
4. *Size variation*—for example, normal versus dwarf stature.

What can you do once you have identified a variant plant? If you are just interested in observation, record the name of the plant, its precise location, the nature of the variant (include a drawing or a photograph), and any other information that you think might be useful. A sample record sheet is shown in Figure 1.5. Somebody else might be interested in sharing this information with you. Either of the authors would be very interested in such examples.

If you wish to collect plants from nature, remember that common plants may be transplanted or have their seeds collected but that rare species should be left alone no matter how interesting a phenomenon is shown in any particular case. What about rare forms of plants? Here you simply have to use common sense. If the plant is perennial, then it is probably best to take a cutting or collect seeds. Annual plants rely on their seeds for yearly propagation. Thus, if you take all the seeds from the plant, its genetic destiny is literally in your

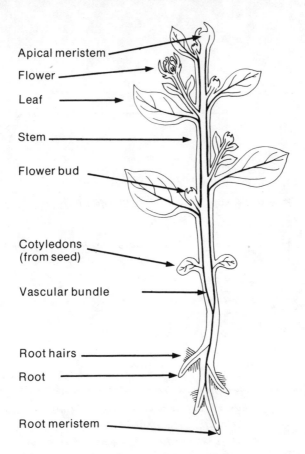

Apical meristem

Flower

Leaf

Stem

Flower bud

Cotyledons
(from seed)

Vascular bundle

Root hairs

Root

Root meristem

Figure 1.4   Generalized diagram of a dicotyledonous plant (a plant
having two lobes to the seed) showing the main parts.

hands; treat this responsibility wisely.

Now you have to decide if the variation you have identified has a genetic basis, or if there is some other explanation for the fact that the plant looked different from the other members of the population. That constitutes the subject of the next section.

CAUSES OF BIOLOGICAL VARIATION

Remember that we are talking mainly about variation within a species. Variation between closely related species is

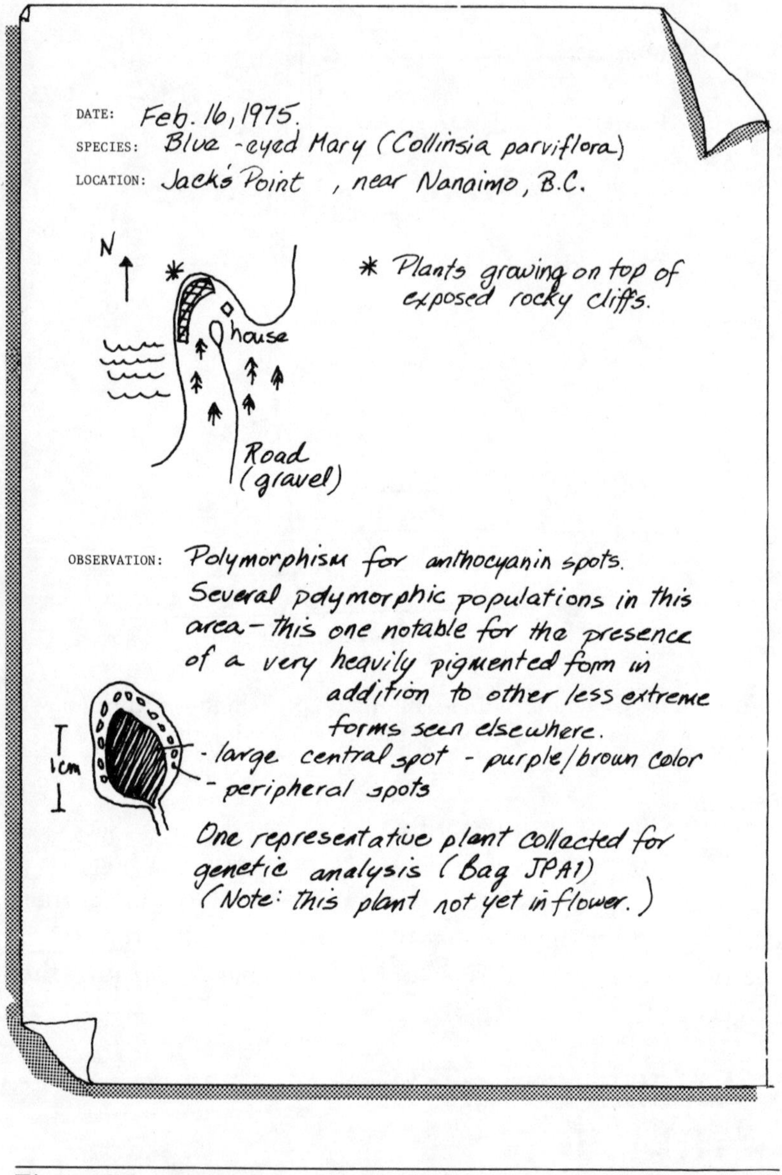

DATE: Feb. 16, 1975.

SPECIES: Blue-eyed Mary (Collinsia parviflora)

LOCATION: Jack's Point, near Nanaimo, B.C.

OBSERVATION: Polymorphism for anthocyanin spots. Several polymorphic populations in this area – this one notable for the presence of a very heavily pigmented form in addition to other less extreme forms seen elsewhere.

One representative plant collected for genetic analysis (Bag JPA1) (Note: this plant not yet in flower.)

Figure 1.5 Sample page from field notes. This page is meant as an example only; the location is now on private property and is inaccessible.

an interesting phenomenon, and one that will be dealt with in some of the later chapters. But by and large this book deals with variation within a single species.

We have already mentioned the role of genes in variation. In addition, variation within a species may be caused by differences in the environment or differences in the development of an individual. Table 1.1 lists all the possible causes of variation.

TABLE 1.1

Possible Causes of Variation

I. Environmental variation
   A. Caused by physical environment (light, temperature, moisture, minerals, exposure, etc.)
   B. Caused by biological factors (parasites or any other species that interact with the species under study)
II. Developmental variation
   A. Difference between juvenile stage and mature stage
   B. Variation within single plant
   C. Mistakes in development
III. Genetic variation
   A. Caused by nuclear genes
      1. May give well-defined classes of types, or discontinuous variation
      2. May give continuous range of types, or continuous variation
   B. Caused by cytoplasmic genes—usually inherited maternally

---

Environmental Variation

A variant plant may be different simply because the environment it is growing in is itself different. In general, the environment may be divided into physical components (temperature, light, moisture, minerals, exposure, etc.) and biological components (parasites or any other species that interact with the species under study). Thus, environmental variation may have a physical or a biological basis. For example, there may be better light or more moisture, the city work crews may have sprayed the area with herbicide, or the soil may be very shallow where your variant plant is growing (physical basis). Or your plant may be infected with some parasite, whereas the other individuals around it are not (biological basis). Environmental differences may exist even a few centimeters apart.

Environmental variation can generally be identified if the variation disappears when both variant and normal plants are transplanted to a common environment. Therefore, this is the test that should be performed.

Let's look at some specific examples taken from British Columbia.

Nutrients and water In the springtime, the sea blush (*Plectritis congesta*) is a common sight around the southern coastline of the Strait of Georgia, where large populations form bright carpets of pink. Off the Sunshine Coast there is a small unnamed island approximately 100 m long where the sea blush grows profusely into very large plants, over ½ m tall, with very thick stems and lush foliage. On Mill Hill near Victoria, the sea blush is found to be much smaller, usually around 10 cm in height. Yet when seeds from both these locations were planted in one growth chamber at the University of British Columbia, the plants were indistinguishable. Evidently the soil on the small island (we have named it Plectritis Island) is very rich in nutrients, possibly as a result of an accumulation of sea-bird droppings.

Figure 1.6 shows the extreme differences in height

Figure 1.6   A sea blush population growing on one of the rocky
outcrops around Victoria. Soil depth, which is correlated
with available nutrients and water-holding capacity, has
a profound influence on plant stature.

that can be produced in the sea blush as a result of soil depth.
The plants are growing on a thin mat of soil and moss on top
of a rock. On the left the soil is deeper and consequently
provides more nutrients for the plants and holds more
moisture. On the right the thin soil dries out more quickly and
contains fewer nutrients, so the plants are smaller.

Temperature   Here again we can use the sea blush as
an example. The pink petal color of the sea blush is due to a
chemical called *anthocyanin*. The synthesis of anthocyanin in
the plant's cell is profoundly influenced by temperature, with
more produced at lower temperatures. In a warm growth

chamber the petals are very pale pink, and in a cold chamber they are dark magenta.

Temperature also affects the production of anthocyanin in the leaves of another Georgia Strait coastal plant, the blue-eyed Mary (*Collinsia parviflora*). As we shall see in later chapters, in some areas many plants of this species have dark blotches of purple anthocyanin pigment in the epidermis of the leaves. We have collected such plants from nature and transplanted them into a greenhouse with no cooling system, only to return a few days later and observe that the large, intense blotches had completely disappeared.

Light   Light also affects pigmentation. Stonecrop (*Sedum*) is often found to be green when growing in the shade but pigmented with red or purple hues when growing in the sun. The effect of light and shade (and perhaps concomitant variation in temperature and humidity) is often seen in the shape, size, and thickness of tree leaves, giving rise to the terms *sun* and *shade leaves*. Sun leaves are those exposed to full sun, while shade leaves are found inside the canopy of the tree or shaded by neighboring trees. Shade leaves are typically thinner and larger than sun leaves.

Aquatic versus aerial habit   Several species of buttercups grow in or near water. As a result, one plant may have some stems immersed in water and other stems growing in the air. This difference can have a profound effect on the form of the leaves, as shown in Figure 1.7.

Parasites   An example of a variant caused by a parasite is the gold-spot form of the piggyback plant (*Tolmiea menziesii*), which is shown in Figure 1.8. This form is probably caused by a virus infection. At any rate, the variety can be propagated by cuttings and is in great demand as a house plant. Witches'-brooms, found on a variety of plants, are usually caused by parasitic infection of a localized area, often by dwarf mistletoe. Figure 1.9 shows an example from a maple. Galls, or plant tumors, are likewise caused by parasitic

14

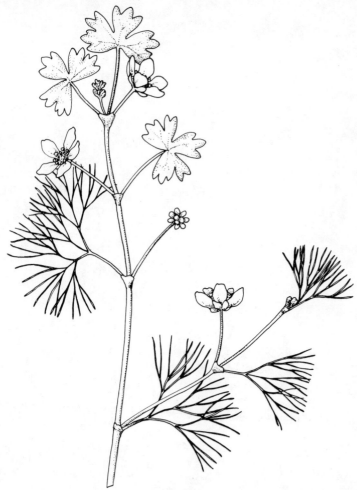

Figure 1.7   Aquatic buttercup showing two types of leaves. The filamentous type results from growth under water; the three-lobed type, from growth in the air.

infection, often by insect larvae.

Developmental Variation

Development, the process whereby a fertilized egg is converted into a mature organism, is a complex process under sophisticated biological control. Nearly always development proceeds through characteristic stages, often called juvenile

Figure 1.8   The gold-spot form of the piggyback plant. This form
seems to be caused by a virus infection.

stages, in which individuals appear different from the mature
form. A good example is seen in the red huckleberry
(*Vaccinium parvifolium*). The juvenile leaves of this plant are
dark green, toothed, thick, and evergreen. In contrast, the
adult foliage is lighter green, smooth, and toothless, and is
shed each year (Figure 1.10).

Another good example of developmental variation is

Figure 1.9   A maple grown from a witches'-broom. The parasitic infection has a profound effect on the size of leaves and the degree of bushiness of the plant. The film box provides a size reference.

the striking variation of leaf shape within a single plant of pepperweed (*Lepidium perfoliatum*) (Figure 1.11), a common plant in the drier areas of British Columbia. Different plants of this species may be missing certain types of leaf patterns. On large plants the lower leaves are compound, finely divided into narrow leaflets. The upper leaves are simple, smooth, and heart shaped, and they surround the stem where they are attached. Small, stunted plants may have few if any of the finely divided leaves and consequently look quite different. This may be a matter of chance or of environmental influence on the normal development of the plant. It is not an inherited difference.

Because development is under such fine control, mistakes can occur. These may occur simply by chance, or they can be triggered by some environmental agent. We are all

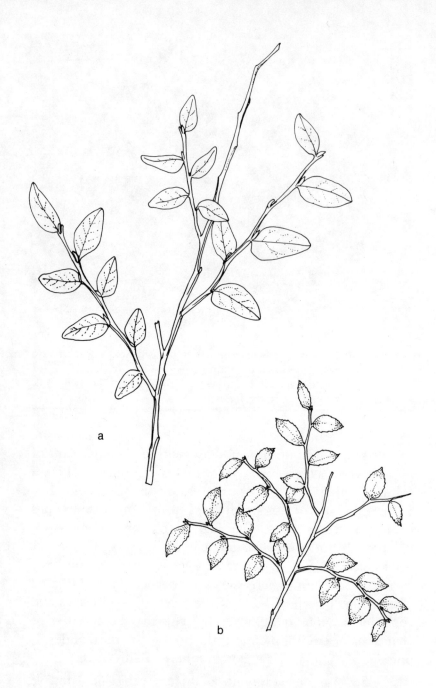

Figure 1.10 (*a*) Mature (deciduous) and (*b*) juvenile (evergreen) foliage of the red huckleberry.

Figure 1.11 Variation of leaf shape in a pepperweed. Much of the variation in leaf shape is related to the position on the plant, but there is also considerable variation between plants in the expression of leaf shape.

familiar with the tragic birth defects produced by the drug thalidomide. Mistakes occur in plant development too. One example is the familiar four-leafed clover; Figure 1.12 shows four-leafed red-clover leaves from plants growing along the side of a path at UBC. Possibly a weed-killer spray was the trigger here.

These kinds of developmental mistakes can happen spontaneously. A good example of this is the occurrence of three cotyledons in plant seeds. Flowering plants are divided into two major groups: the *monocots* have one leaf on the seedling, and the *dicots* have two. For unknown reasons, very few flowering plants normally have more than two. Nevertheless, in seed samples, whether collected from nature or from seed companies, tricot plants are regularly seen. Initially, the plant takes on a trilateral symmetry, which may persist in the mature plant or in some cases may lead to obvious disarray of the subsequent leaves and branches. Some examples from the sea blush and the yellow monkey flower (*Mimulus guttatus*) are shown in Figure 1.13. Presumably when the

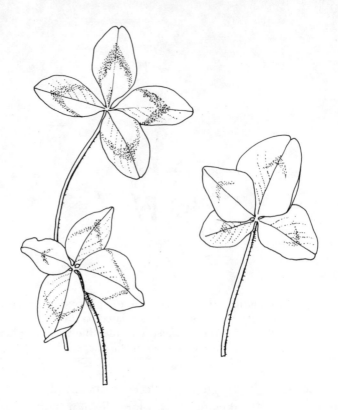

Figure 1.12 Four-leafed red clovers. This is probably not a genetic
          condition but a developmental error that would not be
          repeated in descendants.

embryo is assembling itself inside the seed there is a crucial
stage at which the number of cotyledons is decided. Most of
the time this stage is passed successfully, but all processes
have errors. The remarkable fact is that such errors are so rare.
Considering how many things *could* go wrong in the development of a sophisticated and complex structure such as a higher
plant (or a human being), one might anticipate that errors
would be more common than they are.

    Developmental variation is not inherited; the variants
never pass on their defects to their progeny. In fact this
characteristic is one of the keys to the identification of
developmental variation. Another key is the presence of both
abnormal and normal conditions in the same plant, as in

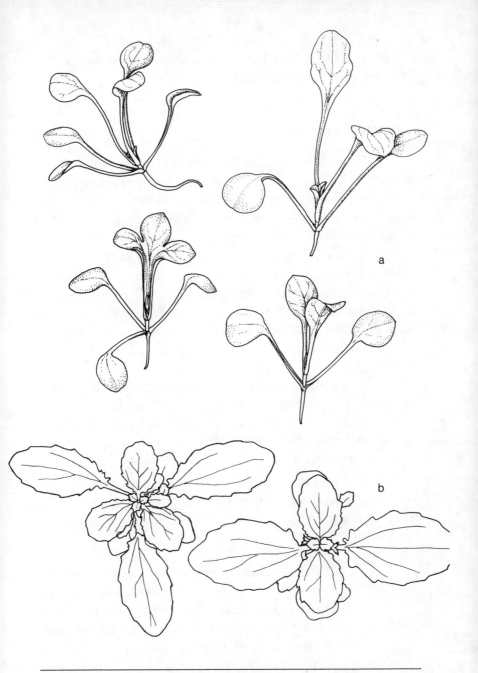

Figure 1.13 (*a*) Sea blush and (*b*) yellow monkey flower seedlings. Tricotyledonous seedlings (*left-hand side*) have three cotyledons and often have leaves in whorls of three. Normal plants (*right-hand side*) with two cotyledons and paired, opposite leaves are shown for comparison.

clover plants that have both four- and three-part leaves; this situation cannot be hereditary.

Genetic Variation

The key to the identification of gene-caused variation is that it is inherited from generation to generation. In addition, some standard inheritance patterns can be recognized. First we will consider the variant alleles of nuclear genes that have major effects.

We have already mentioned that in blue-eyed Mary (*Collinsia parviflora*) plants with spotted leaves are regularly found growing alongside unspotted plants. This type is shown in Figure 1.14. (For a distribution map of this type, see Figure 3.2.) We want to know if this variation is genetic, and, if so, whether it is controlled by a major gene and which allele is dominant.

Using the procedure outlined below, we carried out an analysis of this variation in the blue-eyed Mary. We discovered the spotted type in a seed sample obtained from Jack Point near Nanaimo on Vancouver Island, in a population that was subsequently wiped out by the construction of a new seaport. Luckily, the spotted type is quite common along the coast. Before those seeds grew in our greenhouse, however, nobody had ever reported the spotted type, so we had to do the genetic analysis.

Step 1. *Self-pollinate the two types and examine the progeny (Figure 1.15).* We found that the spotted plant had all spotted progeny and the unspotted plant had all unspotted progeny. This shows that the variation is inherited and must have a genetic basis. (Notice in this case the parental types *bred true* for their own appearance, meaning that all the progeny resemble their parental type. This is not always the case, as we shall see.)

Figure 1.14 A form of blue-eyed Mary showing particularly large and intense blotches of purple pigment on the leaves. Other plants show no such blotches.

Step 2. *Cross-pollinate the two types and examine the progeny. (Figure 1.16)* We found that the progeny are all spotted. This suggests that a dominant spotting allele is at work.

Step 3. *Self-pollinate the hybrid plants and examine the progeny.* We found that ¾ of the progeny are spotted and ¼ are unspotted (Figure 1.17). What does this prove? It proves that the variation was caused by an allele difference of a single gene of major effect and confirms that the allele for spotted leaves is dominant. This is explained in Table 1.2 in which the above steps are represented symbolically, using S for the allele for spotting and s for the allele for no spots.

As you can see from Table 1.2, the eggs and pollen cells have only one gene of each gene pair. This is because at the cell division that produces sex cells, it has been established from microscopic examination that the total number of chromosome sets is halved, from two sets to one set. At this cell

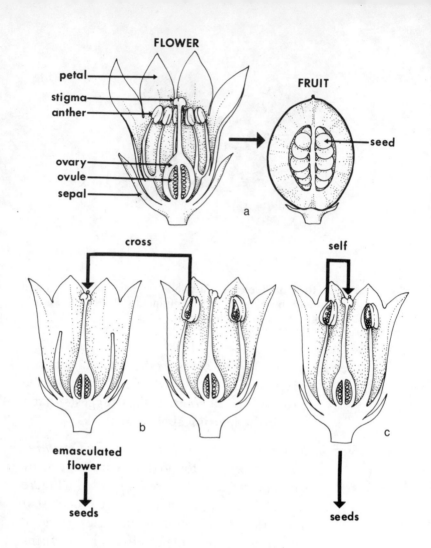

Figure 1.15 (*a*) Flower and fruit structure. (*b*) To cross a plant, remove the anthers before pollen is shed (to prevent self-pollination) and transfer pollen from a separate plant to the first plant's stigma, using a toothpick. (*c*) To self-pollinate a flower, dust the flower's pollen, from its anthers, onto its own stigmas. A separate toothpick should be used for each pollination.

division, called *meiosis,* one allele of the pair ends up in half the sex cells, and the other allele ends up in the other half.

The variation found in the blue-eyed Mary is known as

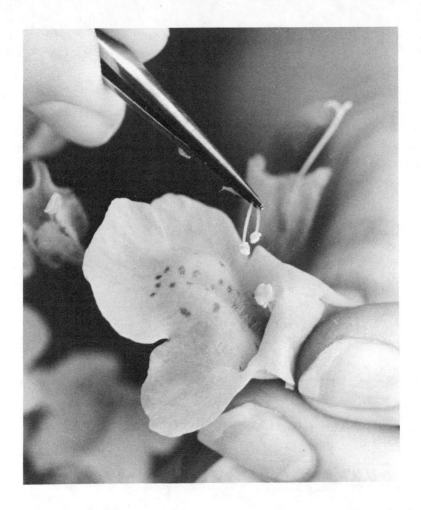

Figure 1.16 A photograph of one way of transferring pollen in a cross, by rubbing anthers from the pollen parent onto the stigma of an emasculated flower used as egg parent. The plant here is the yellow monkey flower, which has large, easily manipulated flowers and is an ideal subject for amateur geneticists. It also exhibits a large amount of genetic variation.

discontinuous variation, in which the variant types constitute distinctly different classes. Discontinuous variation is typical of most of the genetic variation discussed in this book.

What about variants that represent one end of a *continuous* range? If such variation is inherited, then the

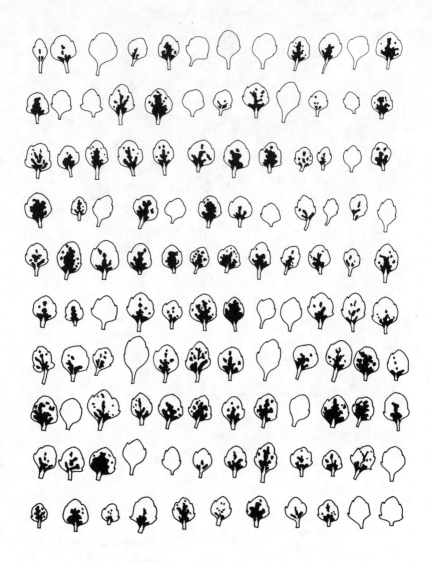

Figure 1.17 Leaves from progeny of a selfed blue-eyed Mary, which was originally produced by crossing a plant with leaf spots to a plant with none. The 119 leaves represent 119 plants. A ratio of 3 spotted to 1 unspotted shows that the difference is determined by a single gene pair. Note the variation in the precise spread and patterning of the pigmentation; some of this is random variation, and some is inherited, showing a genetic control superimposed on the major gene determining the presence of leaf spots.

TABLE 1.2

Inheritance Pattern of Spotted Leaves in Blue-eyed Mary

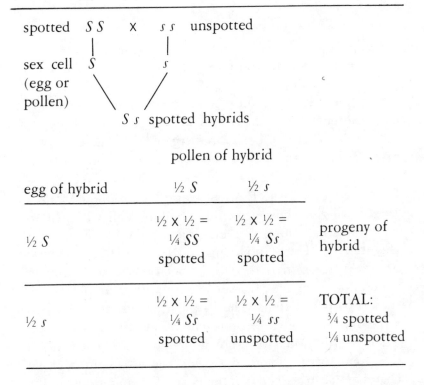

intercrossing of two extreme types from the same end of the range produces progeny that do not reflect the entire range of values but that tend to resemble their parents, although there is some tendency for the progeny to be closer to the mean of

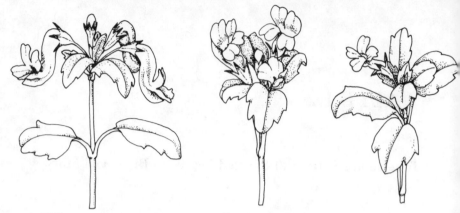

Figure 1.18 Continuous variation of flower size in the blue-eyed Mary. The largest flowers we have seen are from Elk Falls near Campbell River (*far left*), and the smallest are from

the population. This basic sort of observation is one of the working tests for the complex polygenic basis of continuous genetic variation.

What is the result when two extreme types from the two different ends of the continuous range are intercrossed if there is polygenic inheritance? Again, the blue-eyed Mary provides an example. Continuous variation is seen for flower size in this species. Plants growing at Elk Falls near Campbell River had very large flowers averaging around 11 mm in length, whereas those growing in Botanie Valley near Lytton had very small flowers, averaging around 4 mm in length (Figure 1.18). The graph in Figure 1.19 shows the distribution of flower sizes in these two populations and in the first generation of plants (F_1) derived from crossing plants from these two populations. The F_1 plants were then allowed to self-pollinate, and a second generation (F_2) was obtained. Their distribution is also shown in Figure 1.19. The results in this figure were obtained from seeds grown in a growth chamber. It can be seen that the F_1 and F_2 generations show an intermediate range, with the F_2 covering a wider range. This is the expected result if flower length is under the control of several interacting genes of small cumulative effect.

Botanie Valley near Lytton (*far right*). Most locations show plants somewhere in the range between these two extremes.

The complete analysis of continuous genetic variation is complex, because the effects of the environment are mixed up with the presumed polygene effects, and refined statistical tests are needed to separate them. However, these examples illustrate some of the clues that polygenes are the basis of the continuous variation. We will say little more about this subject.

Cytoplasmic genes have their own inheritance patterns. Albino leaves, patches, and branches often appear on plants as a result of a variant allele of a chloroplast gene. (The gene would normally be involved in the synthesis of chlorophyll, the green pigment of photosynthesis.) The inheritance of these variants is usually strictly maternal, since the maternal parent contributes the bulk of the cytoplasm to an offspring and the paternal parent very little. If a flower appears on a white branch and is fertilized by pollen from a flower on a normal green branch, then the progeny will all be white. If the reciprocal cross is made, fertilizing flowers on a green branch with pollen from a white branch, the progeny will all be green (Figure 1.20). This difference in results between the reciprocal crosses is the key to identification of cytoplasmic gene variation.

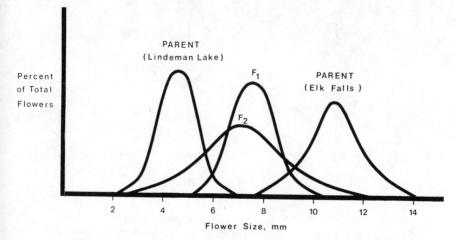

Figure 1.19 Graphs showing the result of crosses between large-flowered and small-flowered plants of blue-eyed Mary. The large-flowered parent was from Elk Falls, near Campbell River, and the small-flowered parent was from Lindeman Lake, south of Chilliwack. As the graph indicates, the F_1 hybrids were intermediate between the two parents in flower size. The hybrids were selfed to produce an F_2 generation, which was also intermediate between the original parents, but which showed a wider range of sizes. These are the results expected from polygenic determination of flower size.

PRACTICAL PROBLEMS IN PLANT GENETICS

If you decide to try some simple genetics experiments yourself, you need to make carefully controlled cross-pollinations and self-pollinations. This is usually easiest with large flowers, but even with them you may find some technical problems. The two most common problems are *self-incompatibility* and *uncontrolled pollination*.

1. *Self-incompatibility.* Some plant species simply will not self-fertilize, and no seed will be set if they are self-pollinated. This condition can be determined by simple experimentation. The problem sometimes can be circumvented by using pollina-

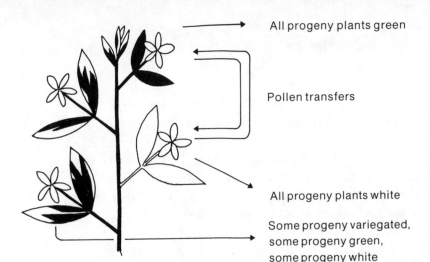

All progeny plants green

Pollen transfers

All progeny plants white

Some progeny variegated, some progeny green, some progeny white

Figure 1.20 Diagrammatic illustration showing results of reciprocal cross involving a plant with both green and "white" (often not pure white) sectors. Progeny tend to resemble the tissue used as the egg parent. This suggests inheritance via cytoplasmic genes, probably in the chloroplasts.

---

tions between different plants of identical genetic condition, such as siblings, instead of self-pollinations.

2. *Uncontrolled pollination.* This problem exists when a flower you are trying to cross-pollinate instead self-pollinates or when unwanted cross-pollination by insects or wind occurs. The first problem can be circumvented by clipping off the anthers before they shed pollen. The second can be solved by placing a plastic bag or muslin sack over the flower in question.

REASONS FOR THE EXISTENCE OF GENETIC VARIATION

Most of us grow up believing the plants of a species to be rather constant in type. In fact, variation abounds, not only in the morphological properties such as shape, size, and color, but also at the less obvious levels of chemical molecules and chromosome shape and structure. Why does variation exist? Why is one plant different from the one growing next to it on the same square meter of soil? Although it is usually difficult to be precise in any single case, one thing seems to be agreed upon—that variation is the raw material of evolution.

One of the main points of Darwin's theory of evolution is that natural selection acts on variants, weeding out some and favoring others. If that is the case, why doesn't natural selection act to "purify" a species so that all members can become perfectly adapted to their specific environments? In a perfect and unchanging world this might be expected, but nature is a dynamic system that is highly variable in time and space. The scene is constantly changing, and the actors change accordingly. What we end up with are very complex levels of variation, all of which probably fulfill some transient role in the evolution of species. Each example of variation probably represents a step in the march of evolution. Geneticists have rarely studied a biological scenario for a long enough time to actually see the changes occurring. We have to make do with the "stills" and try to piece together the overall sequences from them.

The remainder of this book gives examples of variation in the native and naturalized flora of British Columbia. All are examples of genetic variation; no examples of developmental or environmental variation are given. Each chapter covers a different type of genetic variation. In general, the organization is from early stages of evolution in early chapters to more advanced stages of evolution in later chapters, culminating in the process of species formation or speciation. We must point out that most evolutionary interpretation is of necessity highly speculative; in order to make an undeniable statement on evolution, the evolution must be actually witnessed in action, and time constraints usually make this impossible. The evolutionary speculator will always find an opponent to debate his or her views. Reasonable speculation has a proper role in science, however, particularly if it leads to predictions that can be tested experimentally, for that is the way that science advances knowledge.

Field genetics is not all evolution. Many natural variants of the type illustrated in this book have been the source of valuable new strains of commercial plants. Furthermore, many variants from natural populations have been used as genetic markers to tag some chromosomal or other biological process so that the process may be followed in detail.

The observation of a variant should immediately raise a host of questions at the evolutionary level and at the level of the functioning of cells and organisms. We hope that the following illustrations will provoke such questions.

CHAPTER TWO

MUTATIONS

A *mutation* is a change in a gene from one allelic form to another. Mutations are heritable, as the altered gene may be passed on to future generations. The chemical nature of mutation is fairly well understood but need not concern us here. Although mutations can be induced artificially, with chemicals and radiation, they are also constantly occurring spontaneously in populations of organisms. Many are deleterious or even lethal if they affect a gene that is crucial for the normal metabolism or development of the organism. Others are neutral; they have no effect, or the change is immaterial to the survival of the organism. A few are advantageous, making the organism better able to survive, although whether the mutation is disadvantageous or advantageous depends on the environment in which the organism happens to be living. That is, a particular allele may be deleterious at one point in time, neutral in another, or advantageous at another time. A rare mutant gene that is deleterious or neutral may already be found in a population when the environment changes and the mutant allele then becomes favorable.

Because mutations are always occurring, if one looks at enough individuals one is certain to find some kind of mutant. Certain types of mutants are more common or more easily recognized than others. This chapter illustrates a selection of mutants found in plant populations in British Columbia.

Mutants may be useful. Several cultivated varieties of crop plants, for example, represent mutations that were spotted and propagated by observant horticulturists. Others could be of use in basic biological research.

Mutants are sometimes given formal recognition in botanical taxonomy and named as formae. For example, a white-flowered mutant may be named as forma *alba*. Most modern taxonomists do not believe that all mutants should be formally named, since they may not persist and their number is potentially infinite. Nevertheless, they are interesting to find and expand our knowledge of the variability of a species. Most mutants remain to be discovered by botanists, either professional or amateur—so get cracking!

FLOWER-COLOR MUTANTS

Mutations that affect flower color are perhaps the easiest of all to find because they are conspicuous. The most common flower-color mutants are found in plants with red to purple or blue flowers. Most of these flowers owe their color to water-soluble pigments called *anthocyanins,* which are dissolved in the vacuoles (see Figure 1.2) of the cells of the flower. The colored pigments are synthesized by a variety of chemical reactions controlled by biological catalysts called *enzymes,* which are proteins determined by genes, using as their starting materials chemicals that are colorless. Frequently several different anthocyanins exist within the same flower. The different anthocyanins may be synthesized from each other, again by reactions controlled by enzymes.

Mutations producing defective or nonfunctional enzymes prevent the synthesis of the pigments. In a plant that is heterozygous, having a mutant allele and a normal allele, the normal allele produces some functional enzyme so that the reaction to produce the pigment can take place. Thus, mutations are usually recessive. If the mutant gene is homozygous, all the enzyme produced is defective, and the reaction cannot proceed. If the enzyme affected is necessary for the production of anthocyanin pigment, then the flower will lack anthocyanins and be white in color. The mutation may prevent the production of anthocyanins in the flowers only or everywhere in the plant. A mutant enzyme involved only in changing one anthocyanin pigment into another does not result in complete absence of anthocyanins, but in the loss of particular anthocyanins. The result could be a change of flower color—from blue to pink, for example. Mutant genes need not always produce defective enzymes, but the altered enzyme might change the chemical reaction and produce a different pigment.

White-flowered mutants are relatively common in flowers with anthocyanin pigments, but they are very rare in yellow flowers, which are usually colored by membrane-bound carotenoid pigments. These pigments are associated with chlorophyll in photosynthesis. A mutation preventing carotenoid synthesis in a plant could produce white flowers, but it might also prevent normal photosynthesis and thus be lethal to the plant long before it could flower.

White- and Pink-flowered Blue-eyed Mary

Collinsia parviflora Dougl. ex Lindl.   Scrophulariaceae

Blue-eyed Mary (Figure 2.1) is an annual that occurs in the coastal and southern parts of the province, but it is expecially common and conspicuous on Vancouver Island and the Gulf Islands, where it flowers from March to May. Normally the flowers have a blue lower lip and a magenta, magenta and blue, or blue and white upper lip.

We first decided to study genetic variation in wild-flowers in British Columbia in 1975 and made our first exploratory field trip to Vancouver Island on a gorgeous day in early April. The ferry trip to the island was splendid; as we cruised through Active Pass, we saw dozens of bald eagles perched in the treetops.

Figure 2.1   Albino blue-eyed Mary.

Many wildflowers were in bloom in the parks around Victoria, but most of the variation we saw was rather subtle and could have been caused by environmental variation. The day had been rather disappointing, but we decided to try Mt. Douglas Park north of Victoria before catching the ferry back to the mainland. Suddenly, we almost stepped on a small clump of about two dozen blue-eyed Marys with pure white flowers. The plants were all growing within centimeters of each other and most certainly represented the descendants of a single original mutant. Crossing experiments have shown that the white flowers are caused by a single recessive gene that blocks all anthocyanin production in the plant. Heterozygotes are indistinguishable from homozygous normal blue-eyed Marys.

These white-flowered mutants are more susceptible to disease and fungal attack than normal plants. Red onions, which have anthocyanins in their bulbs, are more resistant to fungal diseases than are white and yellow onions, which lack anthocyanins. This suggests that anthocyanin pigments may play a role in disease resistance. We returned to the Mt. Douglas Park site in 1981, but the albino population had disappeared.

We have seen a few blue-eyed Marys with nearly pure white flowers on Sumas Mountain north of Abbotsford. Some flowers have a very faint tinge of blue, however, so it is probable that these plants represent a different mutation. The enzyme this mutant produces appears to be almost completely defective but capable of synthesizing very small amounts of pigment. Because several genes and their enzymes are involved in the production of anthocyanin pigments, white flowers could result from mutations at any one of several different genes. We have found truly albino blue-eyed Marys only three times on our travels—at Mt. Douglas Park, at Mill Hill near Victoria, and on the Flat Top Islands in the Strait of Georgia.

Magenta- or pink-flowered mutants of blue-eyed Mary (Color Plate 1) are at least as frequent as white ones. We have seen plants from Elk Falls near Campbell River and Nanoose Hill near Nanaimo that had completely pink flowers, without a trace of blue. Our own genetic studies showed that pink flowers were also controlled by a single recessive gene. The allele for pink flowers is not at the same chromosomal position as the allele for white flowers, for when pink and white flowers were crossed, the offspring (F_1 generation) had normal blue flowers. We can represent this as $wwPP$ (white) x $WWpp$ (pink) → $WwPp$ (blue) F_1. When these F_1 blue flowers were self-pollinated, the F_2 progeny contained blue-flowered plants, pink-flowered plants, and white-flowered plants.

The genetics of these flower-color mutants is a good example of how genes work to regulate the biosynthetic pathways in the plant. *Biosynthetic pathways* are the series of chemical reactions in an organism that produce the chemicals that make up the organism. The diagram below shows how flower-color pigments in blue-eyed Mary are synthesized.

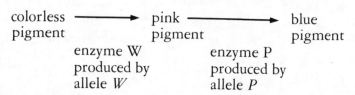

colorless ———→ pink ———————→ blue
pigment   pigment   pigment

enzyme W   enzyme P
produced by   produced by
allele *W*   allele *P*

A colorless precursor or starting compound is changed into a pink pigment by a reaction controlled by enzyme W, produced by gene *W*. The recessive mutant gene *w* produces a defective enzyme w, which cannot carry out this chemical reaction. Therefore, in a plant homozygous for *ww*, the reactions stop at this point and no flower-color pigment is synthesized. The flower will be white. A plant with at least one *W* allele will make the pink pigment, however.

In the next step of the biosynthetic pathway, an enzyme P, produced by gene *P,* converts some but not necessarily all of the pink pigment to a blue pigment. Thus, a plant that has at least one *W* allele at the *W* gene but that is homozygous *pp* at the *P* gene can carry out the reactions of the biosynthetic pathway up to the point where pink pigment is produced. Without enzyme P produced by allele *P,* however, no pink pigment is converted to blue pigment, and the flower is pink. A plant with a *W* allele and a *P* allele will be able to complete the biosynthetic pathway, and the flowers will have blue pigment and pink pigment. A plant that is homozygous *ww* but has the dominant *P* allele cannot produce either pink pigment or blue pigment. Since *ww* plants cannot produce pink pigment, enzyme P has no pink pigment available to convert to blue pigment. Even though the P enzyme is available, the chemical reaction it controls cannot occur because no starting material is available.

When a white-flowered plant of type *wwPP* is crossed with a pink-flowered plant of type *WWpp,* the F_1 progeny are heterozygous at both genes, *WwPp*. Since they have both the dominant *W* and the dominant *P,* they produce both functional W enzyme and functional P enzyme. As a result, the entire biosynthetic pathway can proceed, and their flowers have blue and pink pigment.

When these blue-flowered plants, heterozygous at both genes, are selfed or crossed with each other, the F_2 progeny will consist of nine different gene types and all three colors (white, pink, and blue) in the following proportions:

$$WwPp \times WwPp$$

1/16	$WWPP$	blue
2/16	$WWPp$	blue
1/16	$WWpp$	pink
2/16	$WwPP$	blue
4/16	$WwPp$	blue
2/16	$Wwpp$	pink
1/16	$wwPP$	white
2/16	$wwPp$	white
1/16	$wwpp$	white

or 9/16 blue, 4/16 white, and 3/16 pink. The general statement made here for blue-eyed Mary may be applied to most of the white- and pink-flowered mutants listed in this chapter for other species, since the enzymic basis is analogous in all plants.

Because blue-eyed Mary readily self-pollinates, you could assume that recessive flower-color mutants found in nature have been self-pollinated and you can then propagate them by collecting seed from their flowers. Even if the flowers have been naturally pollinated with pollen from neighboring blue flowers and the progeny are heterozygous and blue, in future generations a proportion of homozygous mutant types will segregate out.

We have found a large number of mutants and polymorphisms in blue-eyed Mary in British Columbia, partly because we have been looking at blue-eyed Mary closely for over six years now. If you carefully observe large numbers of any type of flower, you are likely to find variations. Because blue-eyed Mary is a small annual, however, and populations frequently contain many thousands of plants, it is easy to observe a large number of plants in a short time. In addition, populations of annual plants consist of new individuals each year, while populations of perennials may frequently consist of the same individuals for many years. Therefore genetic changes and mutant genotypes are produced more frequently in annuals, and consequently your chances of finding mutants are higher in populations of small annuals. Annual plants are

Figure 2.2   Wyeth's lupine, normal plant.

most common in areas with a pronounced dry season, such as the rocky hills and bluffs of southeastern Vancouver Island, the many parks around Victoria, and the dry interior valleys of the province. These areas are exceptionally pleasant places to observe variation in our native plants.

Pink-flowered Lupine

Lupinus wyethii Wats.   Fabaceae (Leguminosae)

This lupine (Color Plate 2 and Figure 2.2) provides another example of a pink-flowered mutant in a normally blue-flowered species. Very large populations of lupines may be observed in many parts of British Columbia, and quite rare color forms can be readily identified. Two pink mutants were spotted from horseback in an alpine meadow on Porcupine Ridge near Kamloops one sunny day; not all sightings are made on hands and knees. No genetic analysis has been performed on these mutants.

41

Figure 2.3   Albino camas.

Camas

Camassia quamash   (Pursh) Greene   ssp. *quamash*   Liliaceae
Camassia quamash   (Pursh) Greene   ssp. *maxima*   Gould
Camassia leichtlinii   (J.G. Baker) Wats.

Three similar kinds of camas occur in British Columbia. *Camassia quamash* ssp. *quamash,* with light blue flowers, occurs in southern British Columbia east of the Cascades. *Camassia quamash* ssp. *maxima* and *C. leichtlinii* both have blue-violet flowers and occur west of the Cascades, particularly on Vancouver Island and the Gulf Islands. White-flowered mutants are fairly frequent in all three (Figure 2.3). Where camas occurs, it is usually abundant; therefore, your chances of finding a white one are pretty good.

Camassia leichtlinii occurs from Vancouver Island south to California. Throughout most of its range white-flowered plants occur only as sporadic mutants. However, around Roseburg, in Douglas County, Oregon, virtually all of the plants are white flowered. It is not known why the white-flowered mutant has successfully spread in only that region. It may have been the result of chance, or perhaps the white flowers had some selective advantage there in relation to competition for local pollinators. The white-flowered plants of *Camassia leichtlinii* were the first to be recognized and named as a species distinct from *C. quamash*, probably because the white flowers made them more conspicuous. Often the white-flowered plants from Oregon are called *Camassia leichtlinii* subspecies *leichtlinii* (or variety *leichtlinii* or forma *leichtlinii*), and the typical blue-flowered plants are called *Camassia leichtlinii* ssp. *suksdorfii* (or var. *suksdorfii* or forma *suksdorfii*). Whatever taxonomic status the white-flowered plants are given, they represent a single mutation, which occurs rarely but repeatedly throughout the range of the species, becoming established and replacing the original allele in one part of its range.

Pink-flowered mutants also occur in camas, although they are much rarer and we have not seen any in British Columbia. Since camas is easy to grow, is a perennial, and reproduces vegetatively by bulblets, mutant forms may be transplanted to the garden and increased by vegetative propagation.

Luther Burbank, the well-known early-twentieth-century American nurseryman and plant breeder, once started a breeding program to produce hybrids and selected cultivated varieties of camas in various colors in an attempt to produce showy garden flowers that also produced edible bulbs. The goal of the program was to cross *Camassia cusickii* Wats., a rare species from northeastern Oregon that produces many

43

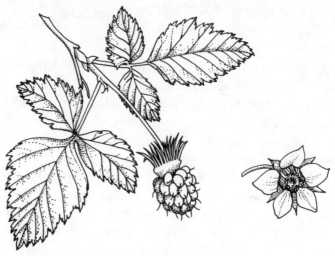

Figure 2.4   Salmonberry fruit and flower, normal plant.

flowers and large but smelly and foul-tasting bulbs, with other species that produce fewer flowers and small but good-tasting bulbs in order to get a plant with lots of flowers and large, flavorful bulbs. Apparently his plants never became commercially successful. Different colors of camas are still available from some specialty nurseries, however.

White-flowered Salmonberry

Rubus spectabilis   Pursh   Rosaceae

Salmonberry is a very common plant in the Pacific Northwest (Figure 2.4). The only white-flowered salmonberry known to us is a single plant that occurs in Cathedral Grove, MacMillan Park, near Port Alberni, on Vancouver Island. We discovered this plant while leading a field trip for botany students. This field trip is an annual affair, and we have seen the same white-flowered individual for seven years now—but no others. To our knowledge it has not been brought into cultivation—probably because it isn't especially

44

Figure 2.5   Viper's bugloss, normal plant.

---

attractive—although salmonberries can be propagated vegetatively. The genetics of this mutant has not been studied, but it is most likely the result of a single recessive gene.

White-flowered Vipers Bugloss

Echium vulgare   L.   Boraginaceae

Vipers bugloss (Figure 2.5) is a roadside weed introduced from Europe. The flowers are usually blue, but pink- and white-flowered mutants are fairly common. We found one white-flowered plant near Merritt.

Figure 2.6   Sea blush, normal plant.

White-flowered Sea Blush

Plectritis congesta   (Lindl.) DC.   Valerianaceae

White-flowered mutants of the sea blush (Figure 2.6) are relatively common and conspicuous. The flowers normally show a wide and continuous range of variation in color from deep magenta to pale pink, particularly when growing in warm temperatures. Some of the palest flowers are nearly white but have anthers that are dark because of the presence of anthocyanin pigments. Other white-flowered plants appear to lack anthocyanins entirely, and these flowers have

Figure 2.7   *(Right)* Normal red clover flower. *(Left)* White mutant of red clover. *(Below)* Normal flower of white clover.

yellow anthers. Although the genetics of this type of mutation has not been studied, it is most likely the result of a single recessive gene.

White-flowered Red Clover

Trifolium pratense L. Fabaceae (Leguminosae)

Red clover (*Trifolium pratense*) and white clover (*Trifolium repens*) are different species that differ in many ways besides flower color. The white-flowered clover illustrated in Color Plate 3 is a white mutant of red clover, found along Marine Drive on the University of British Columbia campus near the trail to Wreck Beach. Note that this does not mean that the red clover has been changed to *T. repens*. Figure 2.7 shows both species of clover.

b

Figure 2.8　(*a*) Albino and (*b*) normal Jacob's ladder.

White-flowered Jacob's Ladder

Polemonium caeruleum L. ssp. *amygdalinum* (Wherry) Munz
Polemoniaceae

Several species of Jacob's ladder are found in British Columbia; all except one typically have blue flowers (Color

Figure 2.9   Albino and normal wild bleeding heart.

Plate 4). The white-flowered mutant illustrated in Color Plate 5 and Figure 2.8 was collected originally near Summerland. Although not studied genetically, it is probably a single recessive gene mutant, like most albino-flowered mutants in plants.

White-flowered Wild Bleeding Heart

Dicentra formosa   (Andr.) Walpers   Fumariaceae

White-flowered mutants of wild bleeding heart (Figure 2.9) have been found in British Columbia as well as in other parts of the range of the species, and several of these mutants have been brought into cultivation. Although the genetics of these white-flowered forms has not been studied, presumably they are the result of a single recessive gene, as are most white-flowered forms.

Figure 2.10 Fireweed, normal plant.

White-flowered Fireweed

Epilobium angustifolium L. Onagraceae

      White-flowered mutants of fireweed (Figure 2.10) are found occasionally throughout the range of this circumboreal species, including British Columbia. Again, the genetics of these white-flowered forms has not been studied, but they are probably the result of a single recessive gene. Color Plate 6 shows a normal, pink-flowered fireweed, and Color Plate 7 shows the white-flowered mutant.

Figure 2.11 Red flowering currant, normal plant.

White-flowered Red Flowering Currant

Ribes sanguineum Pursh Grossulariaceae

Introduced into cultivation in England in the nineteenth century, the red flowering currant (Color Plate 8 and Figure 2.11) is one of the most attractive of the native spring flowering shrubs of British Columbia. The species shows considerable variation in flower color, from pink to deep red, and plants in California nearly all have pale flowers. These paler-flowered California plants are often considered a different species, *Ribes glutinosum,* but the characteristics that are supposed to distinguish them from *R. sanguineum* are inconstant or imaginary. Pure white-flowered mutants have been found and introduced into cultivation, where they are propagated vegetatively, by cuttings. Mutants of perennial plants that are of horticultural interest are most easily propagated vegetatively. If the mutant phenotype is a homozygous recessive, seeds resulting from uncontrolled pollinations may

Figure 2.12 Yarrow, normal plant.

be heterozygotes and thus will not exhibit the horticulturally desirable mutant appearance.

Pink-flowered Yarrow

Achillea millefolium L.   Asteraceae (Compositae)

Yarrow (Figure 2.12) typically has white flower heads, but mutants of various shades of pink are occasionally found. The species is circumboreal, occurring in both the Old and the New World, and some of the more colorful forms found in Europe are occasionally cultivated as garden flowers. We found some deep-pink-flowered plants in Jericho Park, Vancouver, and they probably represent escapes from cultivation. The white-flowered plants they were growing with are probably native.

Figure 2.13 Normal and red anemone. In this case the white is the normal type and the red form is the mutant.

Red-flowered Anemone

Anemone multifida Poir. Ranunculaceae

This is another example of a pigmented mutant in a plant that is normally white flowered (Figure 2.13).

White-flowered Chicory

Cichorium intybus L. Asteraceae (Compositae)

Chicory is illustrated in Figure 2.14. Albino mutants of chicory are apparently quite common. Several have been found in the Point Grey area of Vancouver alone, and many have been seen at Mabel Lake northeast of Armstrong. Chicory is a common roadside weed in British Columbia, and there should be plenty of opportunity for finding new mutants. The albino type has smaller flowers than normal.

Figure 2.14 Chicory, normal plant.

White-flowered Grass-Widows

Sisyrinchium douglasii A. Dietr.   Iridaceae

Grass-widows (Figure 2.15), sometimes called satin-flower because of the satin sheen of its petals, is a small member of the iris family. It is one of the most beautiful early spring wildflowers of southern Vancouver Island and the Gulf Islands, flowering as early as February in favorable years. The petals are typically a rich purplish magenta, but occasional white-flowered plants may be found.

A closely related species, *Sisyrinchium inflatum* (Suksd.) St. John, occurs in the southernmost part of the interior of the province. It differs from *S. douglasii* in having paler magenta flowers, which are usually slightly smaller, and in some small details of floral structure. White-flowered mutants appear to be more common in *S. inflatum* than in *S. douglasii*.

54

Figure 2.15 Grass-widows, normal plants.

The derivation of the intriguing common name "grass-widow" is uncertain, but Leslie Haskin, in *Wild Flowers of the Pacific Coast*, has written:

> Just why the name "grass widow" should be given to this flower, I can not tell, but by inference it may be supposed to originate in the fact that each stem bears but a single flower at a time—a flower widow, alone but not dejected—a widow who enjoys her single state since it gives her the privilege of dancing, and smiling, and winking at every passer by.

In any case, "grass-widow" is more appealing than the scientific name. Loosely translated, *Sisyrinchium inflatum* means "bloated hog's snout."

Figure 2.16 Normal and albino honesty.

White-flowered Honesty

Lunaria annua L.   Brassicaceae (Cruciferae)

Figure 2.16 shows a white mutant of this normally magenta-flowered plant. This species is one of a number of old-fashioned garden flowers that have escaped from gardens and become weeds in parts of the lower mainland of British Columbia and western Washington State. The showy inflorescences make it an attractive plant, but it is cultivated chiefly for the large, papery, disk-shaped fruits that are used in dried flower arrangements.

Flower-Color Variants of Shrubby Cinquefoil

Potentilla fruticosa L.   Rosaceae

Shrubby cinquefoil (Figure 2.17) is a circumboreal

Figure 2.17 Shrubby cinquefoil, normal plant.

shrub found over much of North America and Europe. In British Columbia it is found primarily in subalpine areas. The plants typically have small, five-petaled yellow flowers about three centimeters in diameter. Various floral mutants have been found and brought into cultivation. In addition, selection for different flower colors and increased flower size and petal number has been practiced by horticulturists, particularly in England. The cultivated varieties of shrubby cinquefoil are a good example of the early stages of the domestication of a horticultural plant. Propagation of mutant forms found in nature, as well as artificial selection for differences from the range of natural variation exhibited by the species, has produced a variety of horticultural forms.

Color Plate 9 shows a flower from a wild plant collected in British Columbia in the center, surrounded by flowers from a variety of cultivated forms that have been developed from the original wild species. The cultivated forms differ in flower color, size, and number of petals. Many cultivated garden flowers, such as zinnias, marigolds, chrysanthemums, and petunias, are now very different in morphology from their wild ancestors. Very few native British Columbia species have been subjected to selection by plant breeders, however.

Before leaving flower-color mutants, we should mention "light" forms. These are forms, usually rare, that have a depressed level of petal pigmentation and take on a pale shade of the normal color. We have observed light forms of fairy slipper (*Calypso bulbosa*), Indian thistle (*Cirsium edule*), common camas (*Camassia quamash*), and sticky geranium (*Geranium viscosissimum*).

FRUIT-COLOR MUTANT
Orange-fruited Red Elderberry

Sambucus racemosa L. var. *arborescens* (T. & G.) Gray
 Caprifoliaceae

An orange-fruited plant of the common red elderberry (Color Plate 10 and Figure 2.18) was found on the University Endowment Lands west of Vancouver. Rare forms of the red elderberry having yellow, chestnut-colored, and even white fruit have also been reported.

FLOWER-FORM MUTANTS

Mutations affecting flower form or shape are fairly frequent although less common than mutations affecting flower color. Such mutants may be at a greater selective disadvantage than flower-color mutants if they change flower morphology to such an extent that the flowers no longer attract pollinators or are less effectively pollinated by visiting insects. At the same time, natural selection by pollinators has been responsible for the myriad of shapes exhibited by flowers. And some flower-form mutants that may be disadvantageous under natural conditions have been brought

Figure 2.18 Mutant (orange) and normal (red) berries of red elderberry.

into cultivation by man, a good local example being the
double-flowered salmonberry.

The actual genetics of the flower-form mutants that
have been found in British Columbia plants is unknown, with
the exception of the peloria mutant in the introduced
foxglove.

Green-flowered Shooting Star

Dodecatheon pulchellum   (Raf.) Merrill   Primulaceae

The greenish twisted flowers of this mutant (Color
Plate 11 and Figure 2.19) are so grossly abnormal that the
flowers are nonfunctional. They are unlikely to attract
pollinating insects, do not produce viable pollen, and are
probably seed-sterile as well. Such drastic mutations as this,

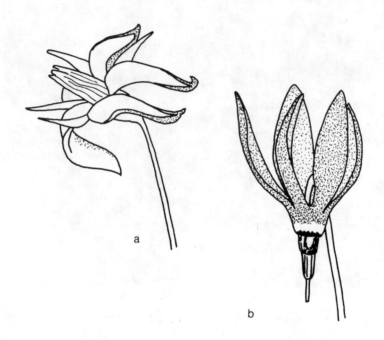

a

b

Figure 2.19 (*a*) Mutant and (*b*) normal shooting star. The normal
color is a gorgeous magenta, whereas the mutant is light
green with some pigment around the petal edges. This
mutant shows not only color differences but also gross
differences in shape and orientation of floral parts.

though not lethal to the plant, cannot be passed on to
succeeding generations and will thus disappear from the
population when the one individual carrying the mutation
dies. The mutant was photographed in Mill Hill Park near
Victoria. Color Plate 12 shows a normal shooting star.

Peloric Foxglove

Digitalis purpurea L. Scrophulariaceae

The mutant known as peloria in foxgloves (Color
Plate 13) is characterized by an abnormal flower at the top of

the inflorescence. The large, cup-shaped terminal flower is actually formed from several fused flowers, as can be seen by the additional corolla lobes, stamens, and pistils. Despite its abnormal form, the peloric terminal flower is fertile and will set seed. The other flowers on the inflorescence are normal in shape. Peloria is caused by a single recessive gene; thus, peloric plants are homozygous recessive.

In a peloric plant all the pollen and eggs produced carry the recessive allele, even those produced by the normal flowers on the plant. Thus, whether one self-pollinates the terminal flower or one of the normal flowers, all progeny will be peloric, showing an abnormal terminal flower. Although all cells of the peloric plants carry the genes for peloria, they are expressed only in the terminal flower.

Peloric mutants have been known in foxglove and cultivated for a long time. In fact, the genetics of this condition, as well as the genetics of flower color in foxgloves, was first worked out in 1910. The peloric mutant is found in populations of foxgloves in British Columbia in very low frequencies, and it is likely that the gene was originally introduced from peloric plants cultivated in gardens. The plant photographed was the only peloric type in a large population of foxgloves on the University Endowment Lands in Vancouver.

Double-flowered Salmonberry

Rubus spectabilis Pursh Rosaceae

Salmonberry flowers typically have five petals and numerous stamens, as do most species of *Rubus*. The flowers of the so-called double-flowered mutants of this species (Color Plate 14 and Figure 2.20) have numerous petals so that the stamens and pistils at the center of the flower are barely visible. Developmentally, the extra petals represent modified stamens. This is a relatively common mechanism by which double flowers are formed, and consequently double-flowered

61

Figure 2.20   (*a*) Double-flowered mutant and (*b*) normal salmonberry.

mutants and cultivated varieties are often found in species that have numerous stamens to begin with.

The double-flowered salmonberry, found by Phyllis Munday of North Vancouver, has been introduced into cultivation and may be seen in the plantings at Heritage Court near the Provincial Museum in Victoria and at the University of British Columbia Botanical Garden. A double-flowered salmonberry mutant has also been found in western Washington and is in cultivation at the University of Washington Arboretum. Salmonberry plants can be divided and propagated vegetatively rather easily, and so single horticulturally desirable mutants can be perpetuated in this way. The vegetatively propagated offspring of a single individual are all identical genetically and are called *clones;* the individual plants of a clone are technically referred to as *ramets* of the clone.

Figure 2.21 Thimbleberry, normal plant.

Double-flowered Thimbleberry

Rubus parviflorus Nutt. Rosaceae

Thimbleberry (Figure 2.21), like salmonberry, typically has five-petaled flowers. The double-flowered mutant illustrated in Color Plate 15 was found near Squamish by Iva Angerman of West Vancouver and is cultivated at the University of British Columbia Botanical Garden. It is not quite as repetitive as the double-flowered salmonberry mutant; that is, it does not have quite as many petals, and the stamens and pistils at the center of the flower are still easily visible. The double flowers are considerably larger than the normal single flowers in thimbleberry. Even the single flowers are quite large for species of *Rubus*, averaging about three centimeters in diameter, so that the scientific name, which means "small flowered," is singularly inappropriate. In salmonberry, double flowers are also larger than single flowers, and this is probably a general feature of double-flowered mutants.

Double-flowered Western Trilliums

Trillium ovatum Pursh Liliaceae

These examples further illustrate the phenomenon of multiple sets of petals (Figure 2.22). Different mutants produce different numbers of multiples. The normal set has three petals. Similar mutants are known in other species of trillium in eastern Canada and the eastern United States.

Figure 2.22 Multiple-petaled mutant trilliums. Notice that different mutants have a different multiple of the basic number, three. →

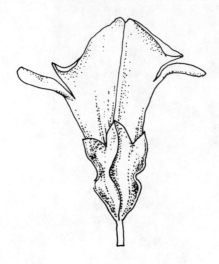

Figure 2.23 Wavy-calyx mutant of yellow monkey flower.

Wavy Calyx in Yellow Monkey Flower

Mimulus guttatus DC. Scrophulariaceae

This mutant form (Figure 2.23) differs from normal flowers in that the ridges on the calyx are sinuous rather than straight. The plant was found on the Flat Top Islands southeast of Nanaimo.

Quilled Rays in Balsamroot

Balsamorhiza sagittata (Pursh) Nutt. Asteraceae (Compositae)

Normally the ray flower petals of balsamroot are flattened, but in this mutant plant (Figure 2.24) they are tubular at the base and flattened only at the tips, giving the flower head the appearance of a spoked wheel. The flower heads are also slightly smaller than those of normal balsam-

Figure 2.24 (*Left*) Quill-rayed mutant and (*right*) normal balsamroot.

roots. The mutant plant was found by Roy Taylor, Director of the University of British Columbia Botanical Garden, growing along Lambly Creek near Lake Okanagan. The form of the mutant is analogous to some cultivated varieties of chrysanthemums, which have been selected for unusual flower forms for thousands of years.

Exposed Keel in Blue-eyed Mary

Collinsia parviflora   Dougl. ex Lindl.   Scrophulariaceae

This mutant form of blue-eyed Mary (Figure 2.25) appears to have an especially prominent keel on the flower, the keel being the vertical, folded part of the lower lip that encloses the stamens and style. Actually, the horizontal side lobes of the lower lip are reduced, exposing the keel more prominently. The plant was found on the south slope of Sumas Mountain in the Fraser Valley. We had been counting winged and wingless fruited plants of sea blush on a miserably wet day in June and the serendipitous discovery of the blue-

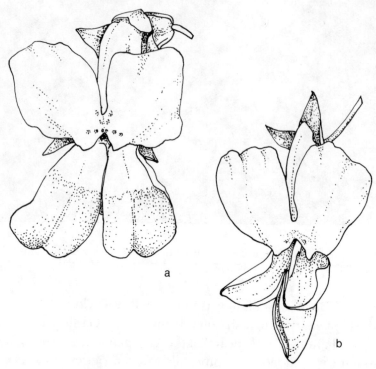

Figure 2.25 (*a*) Normal and (*b*) exposed-keel mutant of blue-eyed Mary. In the mutant the two lower corolla lobes are curled up, exposing the central keel to view.

eyed Mary mutant gave us a good excuse to quit and head off to Abbotsford for lunch and a cider.

Extra Petals in Queen Cup

Clintonia uniflora   (Schultes) Kunth   Liliaceae

Queen cup flowers usually have three sepals and three petals that are alike in appearance. The plant with four sepals and four petals (Figure 2.26) may be a mutant or the result of a developmental abnormality. It was found at Yoho National Park.

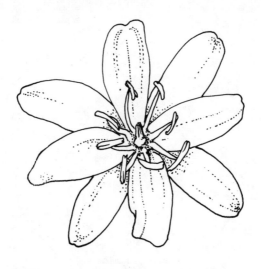

Figure 2.26 Extra-petaled mutant queen cup.

Extra Corolla Lobes in Yellow Monkey Flower

Mimulus guttatus DC. Scrophulariaceae

The two-lipped tubular flowers of monkey flower are normally formed from five petals, reflected in the two lobes of the upper lip and three lobes of the lower lip. This plant (Figure 2.27) produced flowers with seven corolla lobes and so is essentially a mutant producing two extra petals.

Sculptured Corolla in Foxglove

Digitalis purpurea L. Scrophulariaceae

Figure 2.28 shows a flower from a foxglove mutant found growing in the Kitsilano area of Vancouver. The main effect of the mutation is to produce deep clefts in the tubular corolla and prominent ridges in the lower lobe. Unlike the peloric mutant of foxglove, all the flowers on the inflorescence are affected.

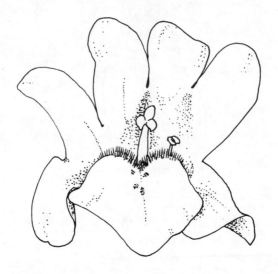

Figure 2.27 Yellow monkey flower mutant with two extra corolla lobes. In addition, the stigma has three lips instead of the usual two.

Double-flowered Large-leaved Yellow Avens

Geum macrophyllum Willd. var. *macrophyllum* Rosaceae

A semidouble yellow avens (Figure 2.29) was found growing wild on the University of British Columbia campus. Among all members of the Rosaceae family extra petals represent modified stamens.

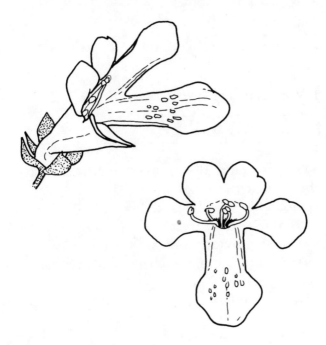

Figure 2.28 Sculptured-corolla mutant foxglove.

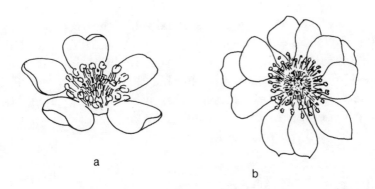

a

b

Figure 2.29 (a) Normal and (b) double-flowered mutant large-leaved avens. The number of extra petals in the mutant plant is somewhat variable. Note also the odd sizes and positions of the petals.

GROWTH-FORM MUTANTS

Dwarf Western Trillium

Trillium ovatum   Pursh   Liliaceae

     Dwarf mutants of the western trillium have been found throughout the range of the species. One of these, originally found in 1938 by Jack Hibberson of Victoria near Hesquiat Harbour on the west coast of Vancouver Island, has been introduced into cultivation as forma *hibbersonii* (Figure 2.30). These plants are much smaller than normal, and the flowers are reportedly pink when they open; in normal western trillium the flowers are white and fade to pink only as they age.

Whiplike Western Red Cedar

Thuja plicata   Donn   Cupressaceae

     Western red cedar is usually a large tree reaching 30 to 50 m in height with flat, fernlike sprays of foliage. This mutant form (Figure 2.31) can be seen in the alpine garden at the University of British Columbia Botanical Garden. The genetics of conifer mutants have rarely been investigated. The long generation time of conifers makes genetic studies of them very time-consuming.

Cut-Leaf Red Alder

Alnus rubra   Bong.   Betulaceae

     Red alder is probably the most common deciduous tree in the southern part of British Columbia. The leaves normally

Figure 2.30 (*a*) Normal and (*b*) dwarf mutant of western trillium.

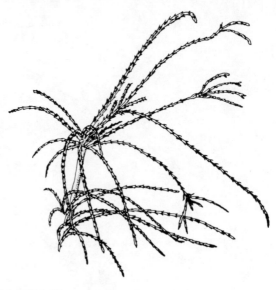

Figure 2.31 Whiplike western red cedar mutant.

have shallow, rounded teeth along their margins. The leaves of the cut-leaf mutant form have irregular, sharply pointed teeth and lobes, thus resembling some black oak leaves more than alder leaves (Figure 2.32).

Cut-Leaf Water Birch

Betula occidentalis　Hook.　Betulaceae

Water birch is a small, shrubby birch found in the southern interior of British Columbia and is distinguished from paper birch by its smaller size and by the presence of wartlike glands on its twigs. The leaves are roughly heart shaped with small teeth along the margins (Figure 2.33a). In the cut-leaf mutant, found near Revelstoke, the development of the leaf is limited to narrow regions along some of the main veins so that the leaves look like mere skeletons of normal leaves (Figure 2.33b).

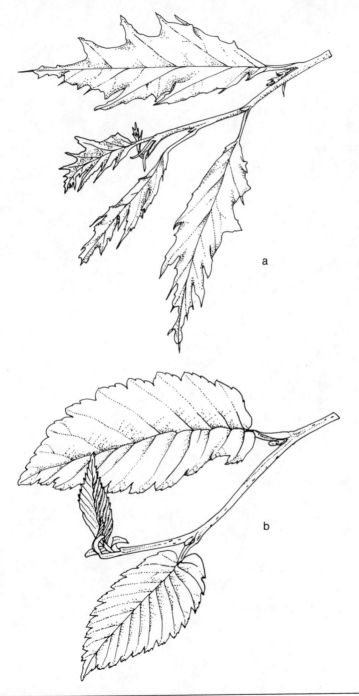

Figure 2.32 (a) Cut-leaf mutant and (b) normal red alder.

Figure 2.33 (a) Normal and (b) cut-leaf mutant water birch.

Figure 2.34 (*Right*) Cut-leaf and (*left*) normal vine maple.

Cut-Leaf Vine Maple

Acer circinatum   Pursh   Aceraceae

Cut-Leaf Douglas Maple

Acer glabrum   Torr. var. *douglasii*   (Hook.) Dippel   Aceraceae

Less extreme examples of abnormal leaf sculpturing are seen in these two maples (Figures 2.34 and 2.35). They are similar to some of the cultivated forms of Japanese maple commonly grown in gardens in southwestern British Columbia.

Dwarf Pacific Ninebark

Physocarpus capitatus   (Pursh) Kuntze   Rosaceae

Pacific ninebark (Figure 2.36) is a large shrub fre-

Figure 2.35 (*Right*) Cut-leaf and (*left*) normal Douglas maple.

quently reaching four meters in height, but the dwarf mutant grows to be only about one-half meter in height, with horizontal spreading branches. Such dwarf mutants may involve a mutation affecting the normal growth hormones in the plant, or they could affect some biosynthetic pathway that is necessary for normal growth. Despite its small size, the mutant produces normal leaves and flowers.

Dwarf Penstemon

Penstemon gracilis Nutt. Scrophulariaceae

This dwarf penstemon mutant (Figure 2.37), found near Elkford, is less than one-fourth as tall as typical plants of the species. While the size of plants is often environmentally influenced by such things as soil fertility, availability of water, wind, and light intensity, this dwarf is a genetic mutant. When grown side by side with normal plants in a garden it maintains its dwarf stature, indicating that the size difference is not caused by environmental factors.

Figure 2.36 Pacific ninebark, normal plant.

Figure 2.37 (*a*) Normal and (*b*) dwarf mutant penstemon. The normal plant is about 50 cm tall.

CHLOROPHYLL MUTANTS: VARIEGATED LEAVES

Black Cottonwood

Populus trichocarpa   T. & G. ex Hook.   Salicaceae

False Box

Paxistima myrsinites   (Pursh) Raf.   Celastraceae

Red Flowering Currant

Ribes sanguineum   Pursh   Grossulariaceae

Arbutus or Madrona

Arbutus menziesii   Pursh   Ericaceae

Big-Leaf Maple

Acer macrophyllum   Pursh   Aceraceae

Hairy Cat's-Ear

Hypochaeris radicata   L.   Asteraceae (Compositae)

Sea Blush

Plectritis congesta   (Lindl.) DC.   Valerianaceae

Variegated leaves (leaves with more or less irregular patterns of white, yellow, or different shades of green) may have various causes, both genetic and nongenetic (see Figure 1.8). In cases where variegated leaves are genetically controlled, the genes may be ordinary nuclear genes or they may be genes within the chloroplasts of the cells. Chloroplasts are microscopic green, chlorophyll-containing organelles within plant cells that carry out photosynthesis, the conversion of water and carbon dioxide into sugar in the presence of light. Chloroplasts and mitochondria, the organelles that convert sugar into water, carbon dioxide, and chemical energy, have genes of their own. Chloroplasts are able to duplicate themselves, so as cells divide they inherit their chloroplasts from the mother cell. Chloroplast mutants are therefore transmitted to daughter cells, but not in the precise manner that nuclear genes are. If a cell has normal and mutant chloroplasts, the daughter cells can receive both kinds of chloroplasts, just normal chloroplasts, or just mutant chloroplasts. In sexual reproduction, chloroplasts are transmitted through the egg and may or may not be transmitted through the sperm. Consequently, some chloroplast mutants exhibit only maternal inheritance; that is, they are inherited only from the female parent.

A plant that contains a chloroplast mutant as well as normal chloroplasts can produce cells of three types: those with only normal chloroplasts, those with only mutant chloroplasts, and those with mixtures of normal and mutant chloroplasts. Easily visible chloroplast mutants are those that produce defective or reduced amounts of chlorophyll, or none at all. Hence, these cells may be pale, yellowish, or white, or at least lacking green color. Plants with all defective chlorophyll are unable to photosynthesize, and they die. "Mixed" plants produce some tissue that is capable of photosynthesis and some that is not, but the plants can survive. Such mutants may be at a disadvantage in nature, but they can be propagated horticulturally. As the plants grow, normal and mutant chloroplasts will sort out differently in the cells, producing leaves and stems with various irregular patterns of different-colored tissue that may be very attractive.

Plants with the kind of chloroplast mutations just

Figure 2.38 Variegated leaf of big-leaf maple. Normal green areas are shown in black, white areas are unshaded, and light green areas are stippled. Each patch of tissue is presumably derived from one or a small number of ancestral cells.

described are one kind of chimera. A *chimera* is a plant with two or more genetically different kinds of tissue that are perpetuated within the plant. The fanciful name *chimera* is derived from a monster of Greek mythology with the head of a lion, the body of a goat, and the tail of a serpent.

Several examples of chloroplast mutant chimeras with variegated leaves found in British Columbia are illustrated. Figure 2.38 shows a variegated big-leaf maple, and Figure 2.39 shows a variegated hairy cat's-ear, which was found in Lighthouse Park in West Vancouver. The cat's-ear mutant was discovered while we were scrambling over the Lighthouse Park rocks one Sunday afternoon with a group of children. All the other examples listed are in cultivation at the University of British Columbia Botanical Garden, with the exception of the arbutus, which was found in Halliwell Park on Hornby Island. All show similar markings. Figure 2.40 illustrates a normal and a mutant false box; Figure 2.41 illustrates a normal arbutus; and Figure 2.42 shows a mutant sea blush.

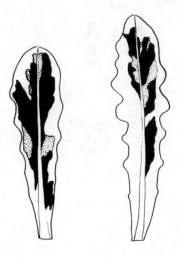

Figure 2.39 Variegated leaves of hairy cat's ear. Normal green areas are shown black, whitish are unshaded, and mottled areas are stippled.

Gold-Spot Dogwood

Cornus nuttallii Audubon Cornaceae

Pacific dogwood is familiar to British Columbians as the provincial floral emblem. The gold-spot dogwood (Color Plate 16 and Figure 2.43) is a mutant with yellow streaks of leaf tissue that make the foliage very ornamental, and it can be seen in several parks, in the UBC Botanical Garden, and on campus. This mutant has been propagated vegetatively and was introduced into cultivation by H. M. Eddie and Sons Nursery of Vancouver. This mutant does not look like the chloroplast mutants previously illustrated, which have more or less random patterns of green and white leaf tissue, as expected from the random sorting out of chloroplasts in the cells of chimeras. The gold-spot dogwood has rather small streaks of yellow leaf tissue, which are scattered quite uniformly throughout the leaves. Such a pattern might be produced by a *mutator gene,* a gene in the plant that increases

Figure 2.40 (*a*) Diagram of variegated leaves in mutant false box. (*b*) Normal plant.

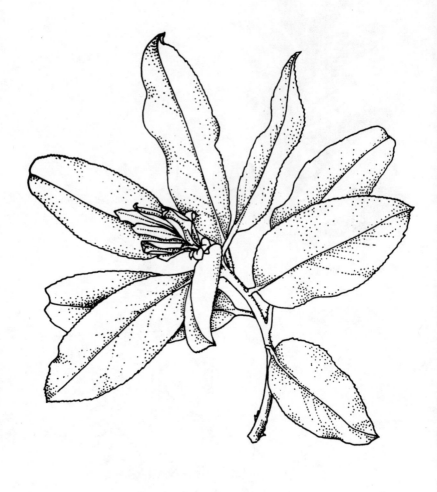

Figure 2.41 Arbutus, normal plant.

Figure 2.42 Sea blush with variegated leaves. The variegation is probably caused by a mutation in a chloroplast gene.

the rate of spontaneous mutations in chloroplasts randomly throughout the leaves of the plant. This is just one possibility, for which there is precedent in other plants. The gold-spot dogwood has not been studied genetically.

CHLOROPHYLL MUTANTS: CHARTREUSE LEAVES

Blue-eyed Mary

Collinsia parviflora Dougl. ex Lindl.   Scrophulariaceae

The normal leaf color in blue-eyed Mary is a dark, dusky green. In the course of an experiment on a different subject, a normal-looking plant was selfed and numerous

Figure 2.43 Gold-spot dogwood mutant showing variegation of green and yellow leaf coloration.

seeds were obtained and planted. When the seedlings grew up there were obviously two distinct types, some with normal leaves and some with chartreuse (light yellowish green) leaves. A total of 25 percent of the plants were chartreuse, showing that the original selfed plant must have been a heterozygote of a genetic constitution Cc, where c is a recessive mutant gene determining chartreuse leaves. Precisely 25 percent cc progeny are expected according to the simple laws of genetics (see Chapter 1). This recessive mutant gene presumably affects the production of chlorophyll, the pigment that makes plants green. We can be certain that this mutation is in a nuclear gene because it is only nuclear genes that can give a 3:1 progeny ratio.

In the Queen Charlotte Islands there is a famous genetic mutant called the Golden Spruce. This is a single mature specimen of Sitka spruce, *Picea sitchensis* (Bong.) Carr., of an attractive yellowish color. Photographs of the Golden Spruce have appeared in several popular magazines over the past decade or so. Although to our knowledge no genetic analysis has been completed on this tree, it is quite possible that a mutation analogous to the blue-eyed Mary mutation described above is responsible for the somewhat similar appearance. The Golden Spruce seems to be faring excellently in competition with normal trees growing next to it, showing that it is a chancy business trying to predict the success of any mutant in the rigors of nature. One would surely have believed that any tampering with the photo-synthetic apparatus through mutation would have been highly detrimental to the survival of a plant. We have not seen any chartreuse blue-eyed Marys in nature, but then the Golden Spruce is also a very rare tree.

PETAL STREAKS

Dame's Rocket

Hesperis matronalis L. Brassicaceae (Cruciferae)

In snapdragons (*Antirrhinum* sp.) it has been shown that streaking of the type shown here in dame's rocket (Figure 2.44) is due to *jumping genes*. This rather fanciful term refers to a mobile piece of DNA, which can land in the middle of another gene (in this case, a pigment gene) and inactivate it (in this case, causing albinism). At random intervals the jumping gene jumps out again, causing a streak of normal pigmented tissue. Like foxgloves and honesty, the dame's rocket is an escaped garden plant that grows wild in southwestern British Columbia.

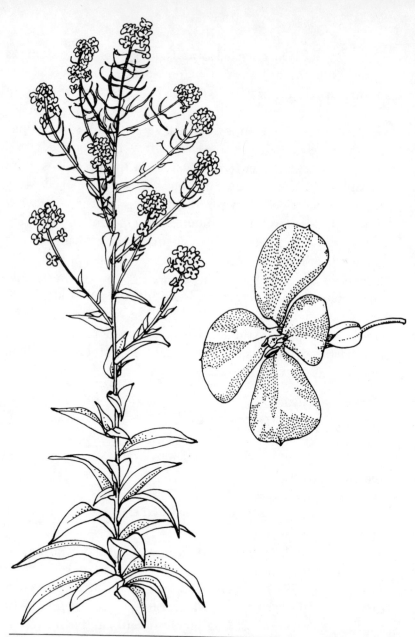

Figure 2.44 Petal-streak mutant of dame's rocket. By analogy to an apparently similar situation in snapdragons, each streak is possibly due to the uncoupling of a piece of inactivating DNA from the middle of a pigment gene; the uncoupling restores function. Once again, each patch of tissue is derived from one ancestral cell. Also shown is the habit of the plant.

CHAPTER THREE

POLYMORPHISMS

Polymorphism means the existence of several forms in a population. In genetics, this term refers to the coexistence of two or more alleles of the same gene, and these alleles determine the various forms. The simplest polymorphism is a *dimorphism,* which has only two forms. Strictly speaking, the presence of rare mutants does not constitute a polymorphism. In a polymorphism the forms must be relatively common.

Although mutations are always occurring in populations at very low frequencies, most mutants are quickly eliminated from populations or at least never increase in frequency. If they are disadvantageous, they are eliminated by natural selection; if they are neutral or even advantageous, they are likely to be eliminated just by chance because they are so rare. If they are not eliminated and are selectively advantageous, they may increase in frequency until the original allele is eliminated. The population is then said to be fixed for the mutant allele, meaning that no other allele for that gene exists in the population. The population is then *monomorphic* ("one-form") again. In the time between the original mutation and the replacement of the original allele, the population is polymorphic, but the frequencies of the alleles are changing. Such polymorphisms are temporary and are called *transient polymorphisms.*

Some polymorphisms, however, are *stable* or *balanced polymorphisms,* and the different forms, or morphs, are maintained indefinitely within the population. Polymorphisms can be maintained in populations in several ways.

The most important mechanism is *habitat heterogeneity*, which works as follows. Any habitat, or area, occupied by a population is far from uniform when looked at closely. For example, the soil may be rockier in some places than others, there may be hollows that are wetter because rain collects in them, or there may be ridges that are drier because rain runs off them. South-facing slopes are sunnier and north-facing slopes shadier. These small-scale habitats are called *microhabitats*. Although different microhabitats may be only centimeters away from each other, they are significant to small plants, especially seedlings. All natural habitats are more or less heterogenous, however. If there are microhabitat differences within the area occupied by the population, and different alleles are favored in these different microhabitats, then the different alleles will be maintained in the population in proportions that reflect the relative frequencies of the different microhabitats and the selective forces at work in them.

Frequency-dependent selection can also maintain polymorphisms. Frequency-dependent selection exists when a morph (or allele) is selectively advantageous when it is rare but becomes disadvantageous when it is common. For example, if predators or parasites preferentially attack the most common morph, they will reduce the frequency of that morph until it is no longer the most common and then switch to the other. In this way both morphs will be maintained, since any morph that decreases below a certain frequency will then start to increase before it is eliminated from the population.

A third way polymorphisms can be maintained is by *heterozygote advantage*. If the heterozygote is selectively advantageous, both alleles it contains will be maintained, even if both of them are disadvantageous when they occur in homozygotes.

Finally, polymorphisms can be maintained by *disassortative mating* (also called *negative assortative mating*). If

92

the different morphs preferentially mate with each other, or can only mate with each other, then the different morphs will be maintained in the population. Sex and other breeding-system polymorphisms are polymorphisms maintained by disassortative mating and are considered in the next chapter.

Polymorphisms may also occur by chance or be maintained by other more specialized mechanisms; undoubtedly there are also undiscovered ways in which polymorphisms can be maintained.

Some geneticists used to believe that polymorphisms were rare or represented unusual situations. Studies of genes for enzymes have shown, however, that virtually all populations of most cross-fertilized organisms show a considerable amount of polymorphism. Nevertheless, some animal geneticists still claim that conspicuous morphological polymorphisms are rare in natural populations. However, we have found them to be common in wild plant populations, and the examples given here are undoubtedly only a small sample of the polymorphisms that could be found by observant naturalists.

In plant classification guides, the existence of a polymorphism is sometimes hinted at by such phrases as "highly variable" or "several forms are common." The word *polymorphism* is rarely used in the key, however. In any case, most probably remain to be discovered.

LEAF-SPOT POLYMORPHISMS

Blue-eyed Mary

Collinsia parviflora   Dougl. ex Lindl.   Scrophulariaceae

Some populations of blue-eyed Mary in southern British Columbia are polymorphic for a gene that causes purple-spotted leaves. The spots result from patches of cells in the upper epidermis of the leaf that contain anthocyanin pigment. Leaves may show heavy, medium, or very faint spotting, or have no spots at all (Figure 3.1). The presence or absence of spots is determined by a single gene, with the allele for spots exhibiting dominance. The very faint spots, however, may be caused by a separate gene or by a different allele of the spot gene.

The leaf spots in blue-eyed Mary are conspicuous only in seedlings and young plants. They tend to fade as the plants get older and may also be masked by other anthocyanin pigments that suffuse the entire plant as it ages. In addition, the expression of the spot gene is affected by the environment. The spotted phenotype is expressed only at relatively low temperatures, below 20° C. If plants with spotted genotypes are grown at higher temperatures, the spots are not expressed. If spotted plants are moved from a cool to a warm environment, such as a greenhouse, the spots disappear in a few days. Spotted leaves in blue-eyed Mary are a good example of how both the genotype and the environment interact to produce the phenotype, or appearance, exhibited by the individual plant.

Spotted blue-eyed Marys are not randomly distributed in populations in British Columbia (Figure 3.2). The leaf-spot gene has been found only in populations in the central part of Vancouver Island, near the Strait of Georgia, and on islands in the Strait. The populations on southern Vancouver Island and the Lower Mainland are monomorphic for spotless plants. On the Flat Top Islands, a group of small islands east of Gabriola Island and southeast of Nanaimo, the distribution of the spotted phenotype shows a pattern that is also reflected by spotted genes in annual clover and yellow monkey flower (see below). The fact that all three species show high frequencies of spots in the same site and low frequencies when growing together in other sites strongly suggests that some environmental factor is selecting for the presence or absence of the leaf-spot genes.

The situation on Carlos Island is particularly instructive. Carlos Island is a small, low island at the northern end of the Flat Top Islands, and its north side receives the full force

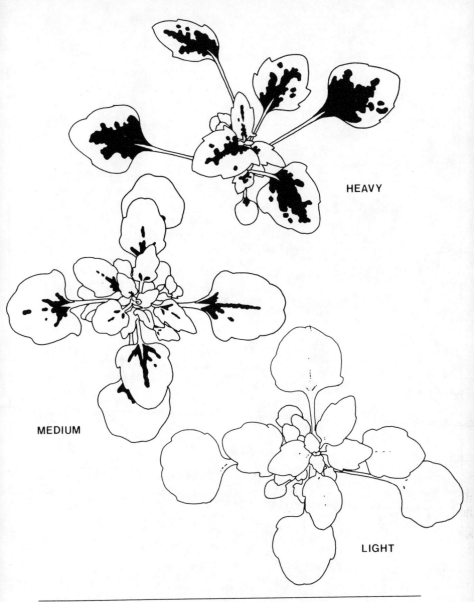

HEAVY

MEDIUM

LIGHT

Figure 3.1   Various expressions of the leaf-spot gene in blue-eyed
Mary. The existence of any leaf spot is probably determined by the same gene, and the differences in the degree
of spotting by complex modifier genes whose effects
impinge upon the expression of the major gene. Some
geographical areas have predominantly one type (on Jack
Point near Nanaimo the heavy type is prevalent), and
other areas have a mixture of types. All areas also have
plants with no spots.

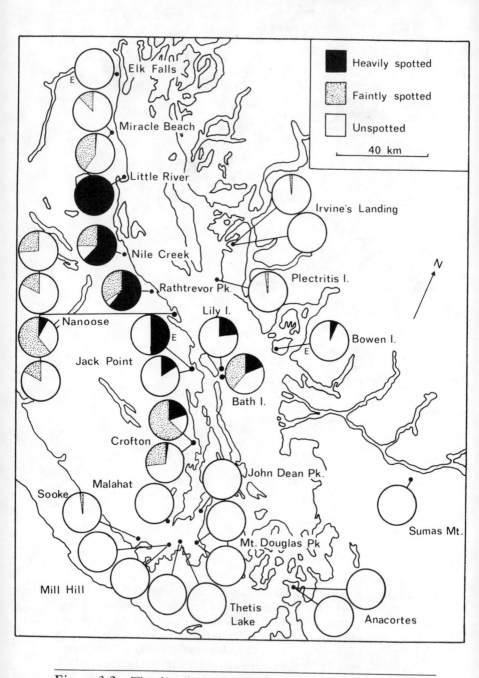

Figure 3.2 The distribution of the leaf-spot gene in southwestern British Columbia. Here, in addition to the unspotted variety, only two forms were delineated, heavy and light.

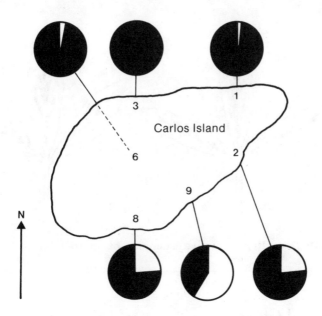

Figure 3.3   Distribution of spotted (*black*) and unspotted (*white*) plants of blue-eyed Mary on Carlos Island. It can be seen that unspotted forms are much rarer on the north (exposed) side of the island. Each number indicates a sample site.

of cold winter winds blowing down the Strait of Georgia. The south side is relatively protected by wind-trimmed trees, and the gentle south slope is much warmer. The frequency of the spotted-leaf gene is much higher on the cold north side than on the warmer south side (Figure 3.3). This suggests that the spotted leaves are favored in colder environments. One reason may be that the dark color absorbs sunlight and heats up the leaf more effectively and that higher leaf temperatures increase the rate of photosynthesis in the plants during the winter. Blue-eyed Mary, as well as clover and monkey flower, begin growing in fall and grow slowly through the winter, forming rosettes of leaves near the soil surface. They begin flowering in March or April, and, on the Flat Top Islands, they die by June or early July.

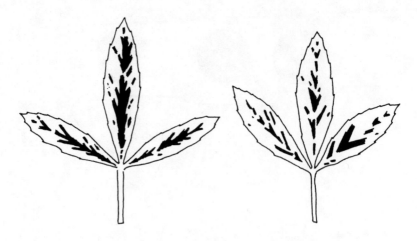

Figure 3.4 Representative examples of spotted forms of annual clover.

Annual Clover

Trifolium tridentatum Lindl.   Fabaceae (Leguminosae)

Anthocyanin leaf spots in annual clover (Figure 3.4) are controlled by a single gene, with the allele for spots dominant, just as in blue-eyed Mary. Phenotypically identical single-gene polymorphisms are also known in white clover (Figure 3.5) and rose clover, two Old World perennial species introduced in North America. We have observed polymorphic populations of annual clover primarily on the Flat Top Islands, where the frequencies of spotted plants in populations parallels that found in blue-eyed Mary and monkey flower.

On Carlos Island the frequency of spotted plants is particularly striking. The plants occur across the island from north to south, and the frequency of the spotted morph is high on the cold, windy north side, increases up to the crest of the island, and decreases on the sheltered south slope of the island (Figure 3.6). A gradual change in genotype or phenotype frequencies along an environmental or geographical gradient is called a *cline*. Spotted leaves in annual clover on this line across Carlos Island are a good example of a cline, albeit one

98

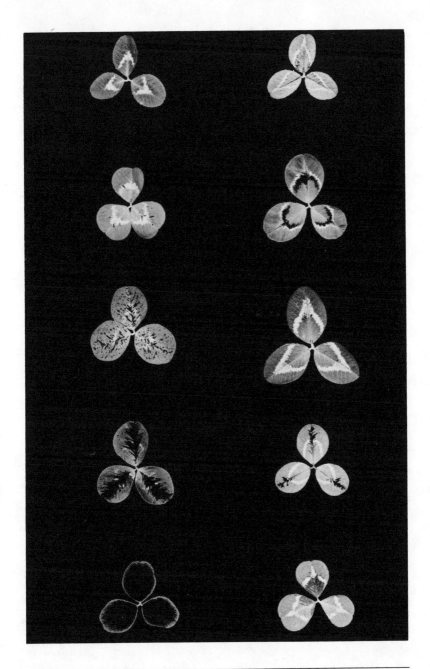

Figure 3.5 Forms of leaf spot in white clover. Do not confuse the anthocyanin patterns (*dark areas*) with the chevron patterns (*white areas*); the latter are determined by a different genetic system (see Figure 3.13).

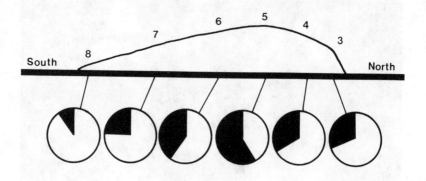

Figure 3.6   Frequencies of spotted (*black*) forms of annual clover on a north-south line across Carlos Island. Spotted forms are most common on the northern crest of the island, probably the coldest and windiest part. Numbers represent sample sites.

that involves a very short distance.

The gradual change in gene frequency along the cline is probably caused by two factors. First is the change in temperature and exposure that selects for spotted morphs in cold, windy sites and spotless morphs in warmer, sheltered sites. Second, the distance involved is so short that genes for spotted leaves from the north side are likely to be dispersed southward and genes for spotless leaves are likely to be dispersed northward, either in pollen transferred by pollinators or by seed dispersal. Since annual clover is a normally self-pollinated species, seed dispersal is the most important way in which such gene movement could occur.

Yellow Monkey Flower

Mimulus guttatus DC. Scrophulariaceae

Yellow monkey flower exhibits a leaf-spot polymorphism similar to that in blue-eyed Mary and clover (Figure 3.7). The spots, however, are usually more brownish in color and usually cover the basal part of the leaf, although the

Figure 3.7   Representative leaves from nine different spotted plants of monkey flower. As with blue-eyed Mary, the presence of anthocyanin at all is probably determined by one gene, and variation between spotted plants is due to environmental factors, random factors, and variation in modifier genes.

pattern is variable. Frequently the large brown area at the base of the leaf makes the leaf appear to be dying. The spot is caused by anthocyanin pigment in the upper epidermis, and, like gene expression in blue-eyed Mary, the expression of the gene is controlled by temperature.

The distribution of phenotype frequencies parallels that in blue-eyed Mary and clover on the Flat Top Islands, but the gene for spots is perhaps more widespread in monkey flower, as we have seen populations polymorphic for spotted leaves as far south as Kern County, California.

Like spotting in the other species, spotting in monkey flower is controlled by a single gene, with the allele for spots dominant. We have found that the variation found in this kind of leaf spotting is due to modifier genes separate from the leaf-spot gene itself.

101

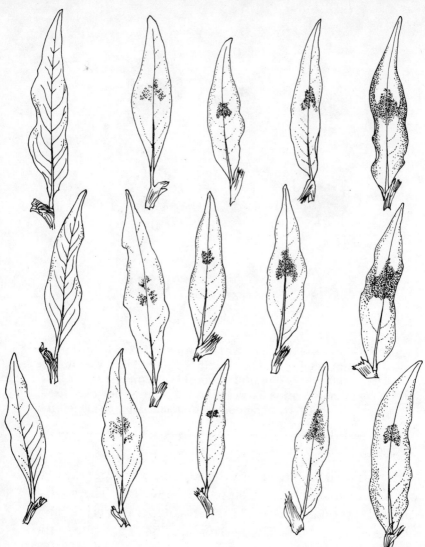

Figure 3.8   Spotted forms of knotweed. Unspotted leaves of knotweed are on the left.

Knotweed

Polygonum persicaria L. Polygonaceae

Knotweed is an introduced weed in British Columbia, although there are several native species that occur in the

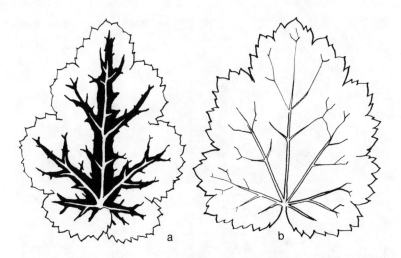

Figure 3.9   (*a*) Pigmented and (*b*) unpigmented forms of alumroot. In the pigmented form the anthocyanin is deposited around the main leaf veins in a pattern quite different from that found in monkey flower and blue-eyed Mary.

province as well. The species illustrated in Figures 3.8 and 3.21 frequently occurs in gardens, on roadsides, and in other disturbed areas. The genetics of the leaf spots has not been investigated, but populations are often polymorphic for spotted and spotless plants, and the spots may take various shapes.

Alumroot

Heuchera micrantha   Dougl.   Saxifragaceae

During a rainy summer hike on Black Mountain in West Vancouver, we noticed a polymorphism of alumroot involving the presence or absence of intense anthocyanin deposition around the leaf veins (Figure 3.9). No genetic analysis has been done on this, and the possibility remains that the difference is not genetic but environmental or perhaps developmental. Genetic analysis will be difficult, as the flowers are very small.

103

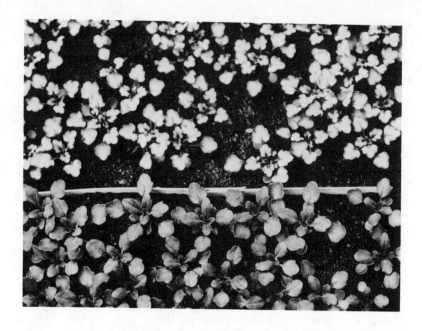

Figure 3.10 (*Top*) Silvery-leaf blue-eyed Mary and (*bottom*) non-silvery forms.

SILVERY LEAVES

Blue-eyed Mary

Collinsia parviflora Dougl. ex Lindl.   Scrophulariaceae

A gene that causes silvery leaves occurs in the population of blue-eyed Mary on Carlos Island (Color Plate 17 and Figure 3.10). The silvery sheen of the leaves is actually caused by air spaces among the cells just below the upper epidermis of the leaf. The allele for silvery leaves exhibits *codominance,* or *incomplete dominance.* This means that heterozygotes, which have both a silvery and a normal allele, are intermediate in appearance between normal homozygotes and homozygous silvery-leaved plants.

In normal leaves of blue-eyed Mary and the vast

a

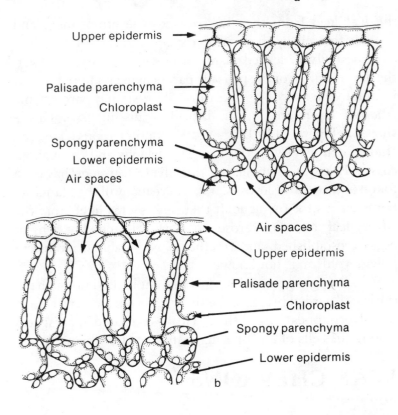

Upper epidermis →

Palisade parenchyma →

Chloroplast →

Spongy parenchyma →
Lower epidermis →
Air spaces →

Air spaces

Upper epidermis

Palisade parenchyma ←

Chloroplast

Spongy parenchyma

Lower epidermis

b

Figure 3.11 (a) Sectional view of the structure of nonsilvery leaf in blue-eyed Mary. (b) Similar section of silvery leaf. Note the air spaces that cause silvery leaf. How the silvery-leaf gene causes this effect is not known.

majority of other plants as well, the chloroplast-containing cells within the leaf form two distinct layers—the palisade parenchyma and the spongy parenchyma (Figure 3.11a). The palisade parenchyma is under the upper epidermis and consists of elongate cells tightly packed together (forming a "palisade"). These cells have many chloroplasts and are positioned in such a way that as much of the light entering the leaf as possible is absorbed in chloroplasts. The spongy parenchyma lies next to the lower epidermis of the leaf, and the cells here are oriented at various angles and have large air spaces between them. Pores, or stomates, on the lower side of the leaf lead from the air spaces to the atmosphere and provide the cells with access to oxygen and carbon dioxide.

In silvery-leaved plants of blue-eyed Mary, however, the development of the palisade parenchyma is altered so that it contains air spaces just like those of the spongy parenchyma (the two layers are, in fact, difficult to distinguish). This is shown in Figure 3.11*b*. Blue-eyed Mary populations have been studied extensively in the Flat Top Islands and throughout coastal British Columbia, but the silvery-leaf gene has been found only on tiny Carlos Island, where many of the plants are homozygous for the gene. It therefore seems likely that the silvery-leaf mutation arose on Carlos Island, but why it became established, and whether it is a stable or transient polymorphism, is not known.

A single-gene silvery-leaf mutant is also known in the cultivated garden pea. Like the silver leaves in blue-eyed Mary, the silvery appearance of the pea leaves is caused by air spaces among the cells of an abnormal palisade parenchyma layer.

LEAF CHEVRONS

White Clover

Trifolium repens L.   Fabaceae (Leguminosae)

Red Clover

Trifolium pratense L.   Fabaceae (Leguminosae)

Even the most casual observer of nature is aware of the existence of the curious white V or chevron markings on clover leaflets. The more careful observer will have noticed that some plants have chevrons and some do not. In other words, there is widespread polymorphism for this feature of clover leaves. In fact, this polymorphism can be viewed on most lawns in the province. It is also obvious that the chevron

Figure 3.12 Chevron forms in red clover. The chevrons are actually light colored; this figure represents them in negative.

itself can take on one of several different shapes (Figures 3.12 and 3.13).

These chevron polymorphisms are seen in several different species of clover and are particularly striking in the red clover (Figure 3.12) and white clover (Figure 3.13). Extensive genetic analysis has been performed on chevrons in white clover. The results show that absence of a chevron is caused by a homozygous recessive condition vv. A V allele produces a chevron pattern. But there are many different kinds of V alleles—arbitrarily designated V^l, V^h, V^f, and so on—producing a slightly different-looking chevron. Of course any one plant can carry only one pair of such genes—for example, vv, $V^l v$, or $V^l V^f$. Where two different V alleles are present together, in some cases the resulting chevron is intermediate and in other cases one of the constituent alleles shows dominance.

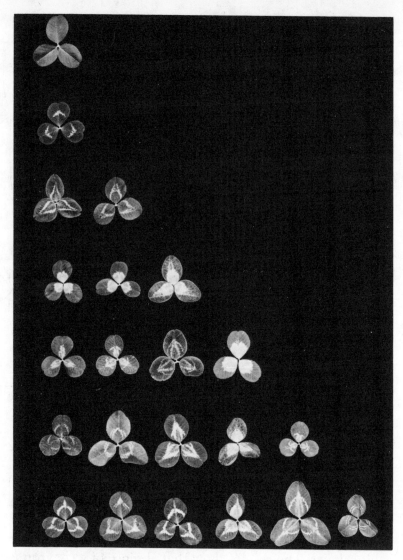

Figure 3.13 Chevron forms in white clover. These forms are determined by multiple alleles of the chevron gene V. Genotypes are arranged below in the same pattern as the leaves.

vv

$V^l V^l$

$V^h V^h$ $V^l V^h$

$V^f V^f$ $V^l V^f$ $V^h V^f$

$V^{ba} V^{ba}$ $V^l V^{ba}$ $V^h V^{ba}$ $V^f V^{ba}$

$V^b V^b$ $V^l V^b$ $V^h V^b$ $V^f V^b$ $V^{ba} V^b$

$V^{by} V^{by}$ $V^l V^{by}$ $V^f V^{by}$ $V^f V^{by}$ $V^{ba} V^{by}$ $V^b V^{by}$

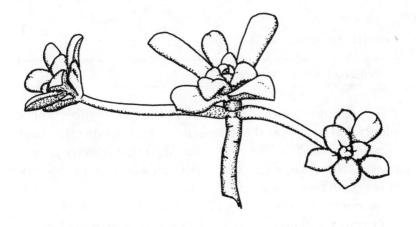

Figure 3.14 Stonecrop.

LEAF-PIGMENT POLYMORPHISMS

Stonecrop

Sedum spathulifolium Hook.   Crassulaceae

Stonecrop (Figure 3.14), a succulent especially common in rocky clearings on southern Vancouver Island and the Gulf Islands, frequently exhibits beautiful polymorphisms in the color of the plants, which may be various shades of green, orange, reddish, or nearly purple. Some of the variation in pigment is undoubtedly environmentally induced, for plants growing in the shade are not as brightly colored as those in full

109

sun. However, plants growing intermingled and exposed to full sun still show a variety of colors (Color Plate 18), indicating that some of the variation is genetically controlled. Nothing is known of the inheritance of the variation, however.

Ground Cones

Boschniakia hookeri Walpers Orobanchaceae

Ground cones (Color Plate 19) are nonphotosynthetic plants that parasitize the roots of other plants, especially salal, *Gaultheria shallon*. The part of the plant that is above ground consists of a fat stem with reduced scaly leaves and the flowers. Plants flower in May on Vancouver Island, and in some populations the color of the whole plant is conspicuously polymorphic. Some plants are dark purplish, while others are yellow. Intermediate plants do not seem to occur, so it is likely that the two forms are caused by two alleles of a single gene.

STEM HAIRINESS

Foxglove

Digitalis purpurea L. Scrophulariaceae

The flowering part of the stem of all foxgloves is hairy, as are the leaves, including the base where they are attached to, and confluent with, the stem. The lower part of the stem, however, can be hairy or glabrous (smooth and hairless), as shown in Figure 3.15. Hairy and glabrous stems are controlled by a single gene, and the allele for hairiness is dominant. Both hairy and glabrous stems are typically found in populations of foxgloves in British Columbia, but no one seems to have studied the frequencies of the morphs in different populations in the province to see if they are correlated with some differences in environment.

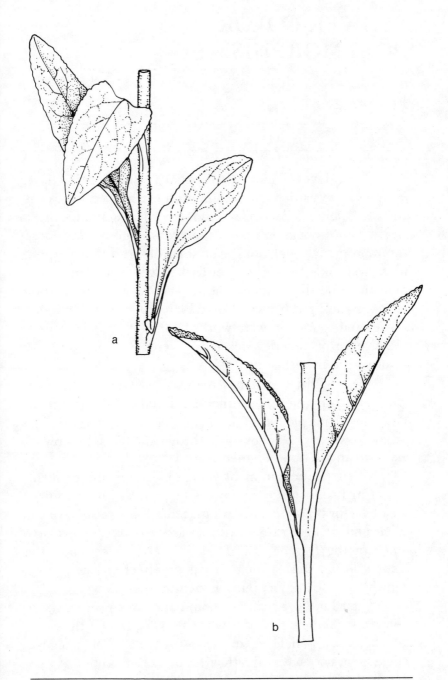

Figure 3.15 (*a*) Hairy and (*b*) smooth stems in foxglove.

FLOWER-COLOR
POLYMORPHISMS

Foxglove

Digitalis purpurea L.   Scrophulariaceae

Foxgloves (Figure 3.16) are native to Europe but have escaped from gardens to become well established in coastal British Columbia, particularly along roadsides and in forest clearings. Although magenta-flowered foxgloves are most common, many populations, even small ones, are polymorphic for flower color. Flowers may be dark magenta, light magenta, or white, and the spots on the flowers may be purplish or yellowish to light brown (Color Plate 20). The genetics of flower and spot color were worked out in Britain soon after the science of genetics was rediscovered in 1900, and the results were published in 1910.

Three different genes are involved. One, *M*, produces the magenta pigment, an anthocyanin, and results in magenta flowers with purple spots. The homozygous recessive, *mm*, has white flowers with yellowish or brownish spots. Its flowers have no anthocyanin pigment.

A separate dominant gene, *D*, darkens the pigment, resulting in dark magenta flowers. So plants with a dominant *M* allele, for pigment, are dark magenta if they also have a *D* allele and are light magenta if they are homozygous recessive (*dd*) for the *D* gene. The *D* allele therefore enhances the expression of the *M* allele. It has no effect on *mm* plants, which have no anthocyanin pigment in their flowers.

In addition, a separate, dominant white gene exists. A dominant *W* allele produces white flowers, even if the plant also has the *M* allele for magenta pigment. (The recessive allele *w* does not have this effect.) A plant that is homozygous *mm* is already white flowered, so the *W* allele has no effect in

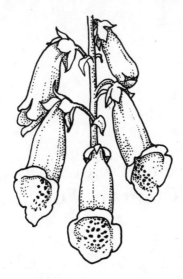

Figure 3.16 Foxglove flowers.

this case. A plant with a *W* allele is white flowered, so the *D* allele has no effect on a plant with a *W* allele.

Although the *W* allele prevents the expression of *M*, the *W* allele does not affect the color of the spots. Thus, a plant with the *W* allele and the *M* allele has white flowers with purple spots, and a plant with the *W* allele that is also homozygous *mm* has yellow to brownish spots, just like the *wwmm* plant, which produces no anthocyanin pigment anywhere in the flower. The genetics of this rather complex situation is summarized in Table 3.1

Some populations appear not to contain the *W* allele, so all plants are homozygous *ww* and therefore the flower-color polymorphism is determined only by the *M* and *D* genes. Populations that are fixed for both the *w* allele and the *M* allele can still be polymorphic for dark and light magenta flowers if both *D* and *d* alleles occur in the plants.

Although no one has attempted to estimate the frequencies of the flower-color phenotypes in populations in British Columbia, it would be interesting to see if there is any geographic pattern to the distribution of the flower colors. It would also be interesting to watch bees pollinating the

TABLE 3.1

Possible Genetic Constitutions of Flower Colors of Foxglove

White with purple spots	White with yellow or brown spots	Light magenta with purple spots	Dark magenta with purple spots
MM WW DD	*mm WW DD*	*MM ww dd*	*MM ww DD*
MM WW Dd	*mm WW Dd*	*Mm ww dd*	*MM ww Dd*
MM WW dd	*mm WW dd*		*Mm ww DD*
MM Ww DD	*mm Ww DD*		*Mm ww Dd*
MM Ww Dd	*mm Ww Dd*		
MM Ww dd	*mm Ww dd*		
Mm WW DD	*mm ww DD*		
Mm WW Dd	*mm ww Dd*		
Mm WW dd	*mm ww dd*		
Mm Ww DD			
Mm Ww Dd			
Mm Ww dd			

Gene *M:* Necessary for anthocyanin pigment production.
Gene *D:* Darkens pigment, if pigment is produced.
Gene *W:* A dominant white that prevents pigment from being formed in the petals except for the spots; it prevents *M* from being expressed except in spots.

Figure 3.17 Midget phlox.

flowers to see if individual bees discriminate among the various colors. We do not know if bees visit the different-colored flowers randomly or if each bee sticks to one color form on each feeding foray.

Midget Phlox

Microsteris gracilis (Hook.) Greene   Polemoniaceae

The tiny flowers of midget phlox (Figure 3.17) are usually pink with a yellow throat, but at Nanoose Hill near Nanaimo both pink- and white-flowered plants are found, and on one grassy clearing on the south side of Sumas Mountain the whole population consists of white-flowered plants. Since the small flowers of this species are normally self-pollinated and do not need to rely on insect pollinators, a flower-color mutant does not have any advantage or disadvantage in relation to pollination or seed set. The establishment of polymorphic or completely white-flowered populations, therefore, is probably the result of chance events.

115

Figure 3.18 Nootka rose.

Nootka Rose

Rosa nutkana Presl Rosaceae

The predominant petal color in this rose (Figure 3.18), as in all wild roses in British Columbia, is of course a beautiful rich pink. However, in a few places many shades of flowers occur, all growing in close proximity; hence, in these areas the species is polymorphic. We have seen a large spectrum of shades in the hills forming the eastern border of the Nicola Valley just north of Merritt. Pure white forms were also seen, but they were relatively rare. These many forms may be

Plate 1   Blue- and pink-flowered blue-eyed Mary

Plate 2   Blue- and pink-flowered lupine

Plate 3 White- and pink-flowered red clover

Plate 4 Blue-flowered Jacob's ladder

Plate 5   White-flowered Jacob's ladder

Plate 6   Magenta-flowered fireweed

Plate 7   White-flowered fireweed

Plate 8   Red- and white-flowered red flowering currant

Plate 9   Cultivated varieties of shrubby cinquefoil

Plate 10   Red and orange red elderberry

Plate 11   Mutant shooting star

Plate 12   Normal shooting star

Plate 13   Peloric foxglove

Plate 14   Double-flowered salmonberry

Plate 15   Single- and double-flowered thimbleberry

Plate 16   Gold-spot and normal dogwood

Plate 17　Silvery-leaved blue-eyed Mary

Plate 18　Red and green stonecrop

Plate 19   Purple and yellow ground cones

Plate 20   Foxglove color forms

Plate 21   Yellow- and pink-flowered penstemon

Plate 22   Red and yellow Indian paintbrush

Plate 23   Brown and yellow chocolate tips

Plate 24   Spotted calyx of yellow monkey flower

Plate 25   Spotted and unspotted farewell-to-spring

Plate 26   Rayed and rayless fleabane

Plate 27   Red and gold salmonberries

Plate 28   Male (*right*) and female (*left*) goatsbeard

Plate 29   Pin-form deer cabbage with syrphid fly

Plate 30   Pin-form bogbean

Plate 31   Thrum-form bogbean

Plate 32   Columbine species and hybrid

Plate 34   Douglas spiraea

Plate 33   Pyramid spiraea

Plate 35   Birch-leaved spiraea

caused by multiple alleles of a petal-color gene or, alternatively, by additive polygenes (see Chapter 1). A similar situation is seen for several subalpine species of phlox, in which many different petal hues can be seen, ranging from magenta to white. These shade variations are subtle, however, and often the age of the flower or bleaching by the sun can contribute to the variation.

Pink-flowered Yellow Penstemon

Penstemon confertus Dougl. in Lindl. Scrophulariaceae

The yellow penstemon (Color Plate 21) usually has yellow flowers, but some plants and populations have pink flowers. One such population has been found at the top of Yahk Mountain, east of Creston. There are several species of small-flowered penstemons in British Columbia that are rather similar and that are usually constant in flower color but have some varieties or populations that differ. The genetic and evolutionary significance has not been studied, but it should be interesting from the point of view of pollination ecology, possible hybridization, and evolutionary diversification. For example, the unusual flower colors might be the result of adaptation to different pollinating insects, or they might allow the insects to discriminate between the different populations. Or perhaps the unusual flower colors are the result of hybridization between species that have flowers of a different color. (See Chapter 5 for examples of this phenomenon.)

Hairy Indian Paintbrush

Castilleja hispida Benth. Scrophulariaceae

Populations of Indian paintbrush at Botanie Valley near Lytton are spectacularly polymorphic for flower color (Color Plate 22 and Figure 3.19). Actually, the bright-colored

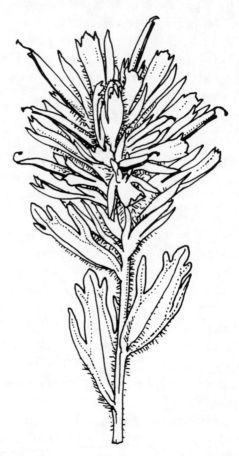

Figure 3.19 Hairy Indian paintbrush.

parts of the inflorescence are the sepals of the flowers and the leafy bracts associated with each flower. They may be yellow, bright red, or various intermediate shades of orange. The genetics of this variation has not been worked out, but it is probably controlled by one or two genes, with alleles for red or yellow pigment and heterozygotes exhibiting the intermediate orange inflorescence color. Several other species of Indian paintbrush in British Columbia also exhibit variation in inflorescence color, which is one of the reasons the different species are difficult to distinguish.

Figure 3.20 Dove's foot cranesbill.

Dove's Foot Cranesbill

Geranium molle L. Geraniaceae

Dove's foot cranesbill (Figure 3.20) is an introduced plant in British Columbia and usually has magenta to pink flowers. But populations polymorphic for magenta- and white-flowered plants occur—for example, at Redwood Park in Delta. The white-flowered plants probably represent recessive homozygotes at a single gene that have become established by chance in this population.

Figure 3.21 Knotweed plant.

Knotweed

Polygonum persicaria L.   Polygonaceae

Common knotweed (Figure 3.21) is a weed introduced from Europe and is usually found in gardens, on farms, or in other cultivated areas. It and some other weedy species of knotweed are polymorphic for pink or white flowers. Genetic analysis of flower color in knotweed has not been done.

Chocolate Tips

Lomatium dissectum   (Nutt.) Math. & Const.   Apiaceae (Umbelliferae)

Chocolate tips (Color Plate 23) occurs sporadically in southern British Columbia, being common in parts of the Okanagan Valley and near Lytton. The flowers are usually brownish purple, but some populations have both brownish purple and yellow flowers. Although the difference is likely to be controlled by a single gene, the genetics has not been studied. Several other species of *Lomatium* are polymorphic for yellow and purple flowers or yellow and white flowers.

CALYX-SPOT POLYMORPHISM

Yellow Monkey Flower

Mimulus guttatus   DC.   Scrophulariaceae

Yellow monkey flower is a variable species in which many mutants and polymorphisms can be seen. One polymorphism frequent in populations on Vancouver Island and the Gulf Islands, and also at some mainland locations, is the presence or absence of small peppered spots of reddish anthocyanin on the calyx of the flowers (Color Plate 24 and Figure 3.22). Genetic analysis has shown that the presence of these spots is due to a single dominant gene, but it is a separate gene from the one responsible for spotted leaves in yellow monkey flower. The expression of calyx spots is variable, from fine pinpricks to large blotches. Sometimes the whole plant is spotted, apparently involving the same genetic mechanism (Figure 3.23).

121

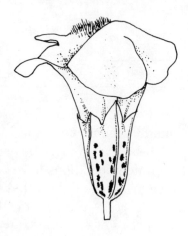

Figure 3.22 Spotted-calyx form of yellow monkey flower.

Figure 3.23 Condition in yellow monkey flower in which spots, apparently similar to the calyx spots, are found throughout the plant.

GENERAL ANTHOCYANIN POLYMORPHISM

Yellow Monkey Flower

Mimulus guttatus DC. Scrophulariaceae

Monkey flower is polymorphic for yet another aspect of its anthocyanin pigmentation. This is a general kind of anthocyanin deposition in the stems, petioles, and calyxes (Figure 3.24). The presence or absence of this pigmentation is determined by one pair of alleles, with presence dominant to absence. Anthocyanin deposition in monkey flower is yet another example of gene-environment interaction, for the pigment is not deposited unless direct sunlight falls on the plant. This can be seen in the figure, which shows no pigment in the shaded areas.

Thus, in all, we have seen three polymorphisms in yellow monkey flower, all involving anthocyanin—leaf spots, calyx spots, and general pigmentation. These polymorphisms involve separate controls over anthocyanin deposition, determined by separate genetic systems; this separateness is easily demonstrated by showing that plants that have, say, a leaf spot may have no calyx spots or general pigmentation. None of these plants can be thought of as an anthocyaninless mutant, such as albino blue-eyed Mary, for even plants lacking anthocyanin in all three green-tissue deposition systems still have the characteristic anthocyanin spots on the lower lip of the flower.

Figure 3.24 Typical distribution of general anthocyanin deposition in yellow monkey flower.

PETAL-SPOT POLYMORPHISM

Farewell-to-Spring

Clarkia amoena (Lehm.) Nels. & Macbr. ssp. *lindleyi*
(Dougl.) Lewis & Lewis Onagraceae

Farewell-to-spring occurs in dry clearings in south-western British Columbia, flowering in June and early July,

Figure 3.25 Farewell-to-spring.

after most of the other spring annuals have finished flowering. Some populations are polymorphic for a gene that produces a large purple spot near the base of each petal (Color Plate 25 and Figure 3.25). Other populations are monomorphic. The genetics of the petal spot in farewell-to-spring has not been analyzed. Several other species of farewell-to-spring in California, however, exhibit a similar petal-spot polymorphism, and it has been shown to be controlled by a single gene, with spots dominant to absence of spots. In all probability petal spots in farewell-to-spring are controlled by an identical gene.

RAY POLYMORPHISMS

Rayed and Rayless Cut-Leaved Fleabane

Erigeron compositus   Pursh   Asteraceae (Compositae)

Fleabane is a member of the aster or composite family, which is characterized by heads of small flowers that functionally resemble single flowers. In many composites the inner flowers of the heads, called disk flowers, are small and tubular, while the outer flowers, called ray flowers, are large, broadly expanded, and petallike. Some composites have only disk flowers, but most have both disk and ray flowers in each head. Polymorphisms for plants with and without ray flowers, or with very reduced ray flowers, are known in several composites.

Such a polymorphism occurs in cut-leaved fleabane in south central British Columbia (Color Plate 26 and Figure 3.26). In this species the rayless flowers are not actually rayless but have such tiny rays that they are rarely visible unless the head is dissected. The rayed and "rayless" flowers look conspicuously different and might be expected to differ in their attractiveness to pollinating insects. However, this species is composed of a number of *agamospermous* forms, or forms that produce seeds without fertilization (virgin birth, as it were). Thus, pollinators may or may not be needed.

Neither the genetics nor the pollination biology of this polymorphism has been studied in this species. However, the common groundsel, *Senecio vulgaris* (Figure 3.27), is also polymorphic for rayed and rayless flower heads in parts of Great Britain, and the genetics of this species has been studied. In the common groundsel a single gene controls the presence of ray flowers, and it shows incomplete dominance. Plants homozygous for the ray allele have large rays, plants homozygous for the rayless allele have rayless flowers, and heterozygotes have very small, inconspicuous rays. In addition,

Figure 3.26 (*Right*) Rayed and (*left*) rayless forms of cut-leaved fleabane.

there is good evidence that plants with conspicuous ray flowers are cross-pollinated by insects to a greater extent than rayless flowered plants, which are almost totally self-pollinated. In British Columbia we have seen only the rayless morph of common groundsel.

Figure 3.27 Common groundsel with rayless flowers.

Narrow-rayed and Wide-rayed Moresby Butterweed

Senecio cymbalarioides Bueck ssp. *moresbiensis* Calder & Taylor
Asteraceae (Compositae)

We have been told about this polymorphism by Dr. Rolf Mathews of Simon Fraser University. These two highly distinct forms of butterweed are to be found on the Queen Charlotte Islands. Although this is the only example in the book from that botanical wonderland, those islands are sure to yield many other examples of interesting genetic variants. Butterweed is illustrated in Figure 3.28.

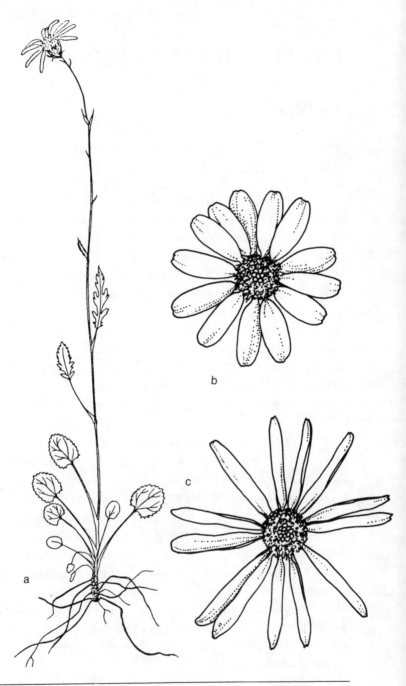

Figure 3.28 Moresby butterweed. *(a)* Habit of plant. *(b)* Wide-rayed flower. *(c)* Narrow-rayed flower.

FRUIT POLYMORPHISMS

Sea Blush

Plectritis congesta   (Lindl.) DC.   Valerianaceae
Plectritis brachystemon   F. & M.

Plants of the genus *Plectritis* exhibit an incredible amount of variation in their small, dry, seedlike fruits. Some of the fruit types are so distinctive that many individual species were named according to these differences, until it was recognized that they merely represented genetic polymorphisms within populations. The fruits exhibit a variety of shapes, involving the presence or absence of two earlike wings, the shape and curvature of the wings, the presence and location of hairs on the fruits, and the color, which ranges from pale straw color through yellowish and golden brown to dark brown. Length also varies from two to four millimeters. Some of the shapes and hair patterns are illustrated in Figure 3.29.

These characters are inherited—as can be seen if selfed offspring are grown in the same environment for several generations—but the actual genetics of most of the characters has not yet been worked out. In British Columbia, both *P. congesta* and *P. brachystemon* show these fruit variations. Although many different morphs are typically found in populations of *P. congesta,* populations of *P. brachystemon* are usually relatively uniform and often consist of plants that all have identical fruits. The reason for this is that *P. congesta* routinely cross-pollinates and *P. brachystemon* is highly self-pollinated, and genetic variation is more easily lost from highly self-pollinated populations, either by selection or by random events.

Although the genetics of wing shape is not known, the polymorphism for the presence or absence of wings has been

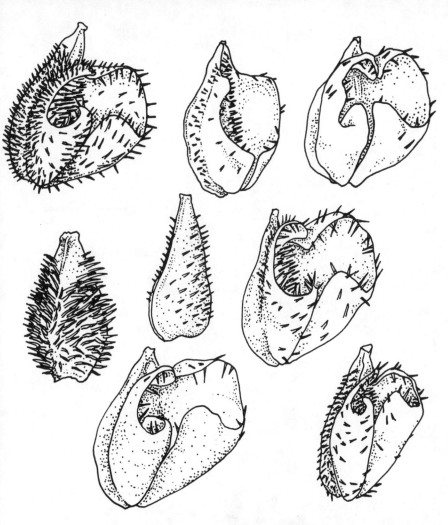

Figure 3.29 Sea blush plants are highly variable with respect to various inherited fruit shapes and hair patterns. A sample of types is shown in this diagram.

studied quite thoroughly. It is controlled by a single gene, with the allele for wings dominant to the allele for the absence of wings. The mode of inheritance is the same in both *P. congesta* and *P. brachystemon*. A single dominant gene for winged fruits also occurs in some species in the closely related genus *Valerianella* in the southeastern United States, suggesting that this polymorphism may be older than the evolutionary divergence of the two genera.

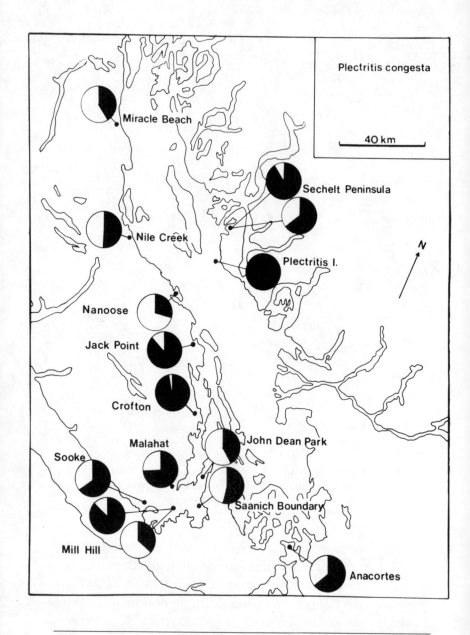

Figure 3.30 Distribution map of the occurrence of winged (*black*) and wingless (*white*) fruit forms of *Plectritis congesta* throughout southwestern British Columbia.

The frequencies of winged and wingless fruited plants vary dramatically in different populations of sea blush. In *P. congesta* we have found populations with phenotype frequencies ranging from only 29 percent winged to 100 percent winged, but nearly all have both forms present (Figures 3.30 and 3.31). There is no apparent geographical pattern to the distribution of frequencies. This does not, however, eliminate the possibility that more subtle characteristics of the individual habitats might be correlated with frequency of winged plants.

In *P. brachystemon,* most populations are either completely winged or completely wingless (Figure 3.32). Populations on southeastern Vancouver Island are constant for the wingless fruited allele, while populations on the west coast or farther north are constant or nearly always constant for the winged allele. We have seen polymorphic populations on Sumas Mountain and the Sechelt Peninsula, but even in these populations the two forms are not randomly distributed. Rather, one finds distinct patches where one fruit form or the other predominates. This could be caused by microhabitat differences within the population favoring one form or the other, but this hypothesis has not been tested. Since *P. brachystemon* (Figure 3.33) normally self-pollinates, however, nearly all of the plants are homozygous, and the offspring will be like their parent. Since most seeds are distributed near the parent plant, clumps of plants of the same form are bound to become established.

The fruit-wing polymorphism in *P. congesta* is one of the few cases where there is evidence that the polymorphism is maintained by heterozygote advantage. (Wingless fruited plants are homozygous for the recessive wingless allele, with genotype *ww,* while winged fruited plants can be either homozygous dominant *WW* or heterozygous *Ww.*) Genetic studies of natural populations have shown that there are more heterozygotes than expected according to the laws of population genetics. In addition, studies of the three genotypes grown under uniform experimental conditions have confirmed that heterozygotes are larger and have more inflorescences. Since heterozygotes have both alleles in their genotype, if they

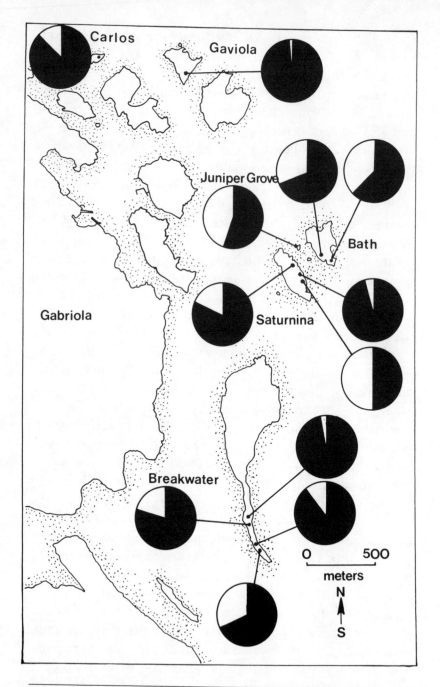

Figure 3.31 Distribution map of the occurrence of winged (*black*) and wingless (*white*) fruit forms of *Plectritis congesta* on the Flat Top Islands.

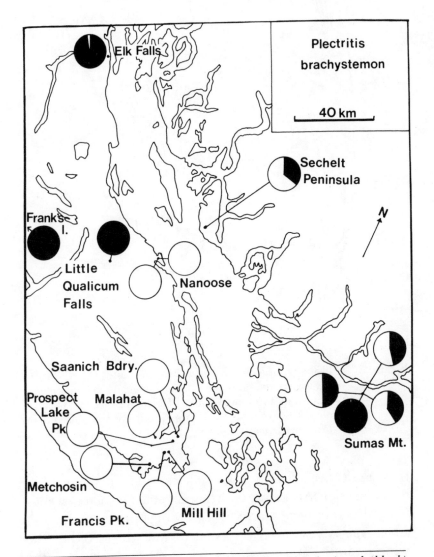

Figure 3.32 Distribution map of the occurrence of winged (*black*) and wingless (*white*) fruit forms of *Plectritis brachystemon* throughout southwestern British Columbia.

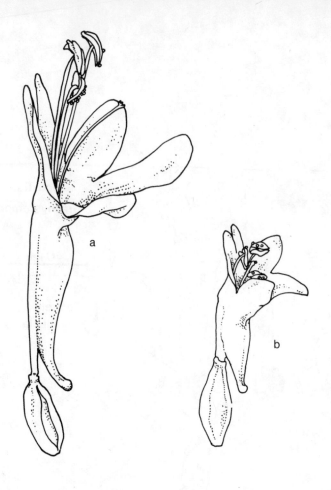

Figure 3.33 Flowers of (*a*) *Plectritis congesta* and (*b*) *Plectritis brachystemon*. Note the different sizes and the protrusion of anthers and stamens in the *Plectritis congesta*. It is also more fragrant and much more intensely pigmented than *Plectritis brachystemon*.

have a selective advantage both alleles will be maintained in the population. Also, since both homozygous and heterozygous winged plants have identical fruit wings, the heterozygote advantage is not directly related to the wings. Either the winged and wingless alleles have other effects on the development or physiology of the plants, or the advantageous effects of heterozygosity are not caused by the fruit-wing locus itself but are caused by other genes that are tightly linked with it.

The demonstrated heterozygote advantage is sufficient to maintain polymorphic populations in *P. congesta,* and the high percentage of polymorphic populations that exists is consistent with this explanation. *Plectritis brachystemon,* however, so frequently self-pollinates that virtually all of the plants in natural populations are homozygous. Thus, there are no heterozygotes to have an advantage. Where cross-pollination is so rare that heterozygotes are seldom produced, their advantage is not great enough to prevent one allele from being lost from the population by either selection or random genetic events.

FRUIT-COLOR POLYMORPHISMS

Red and Gold Salmonberry

Rubus spectabilis   Pursh   Rosaceae

Salmonberry fruits are either golden yellow or red (Color Plate 27). The red color is due to the presence of anthocyanin pigments, and the darkness of the red is somewhat variable, depending on the amount of pigment. Some fruits are so dark they are almost purplish. The fruit color is probably controlled by a single gene, with the allele for red fruits dominant and the allele for gold fruits recessive (this is inferred from analogy with related *Rubus* species). Since salmonberries are so common in coastal British Columbia, they provide one of the most commonly observed and conspicuous polymorphisms. Many people who have seen the two forms, however, just assume that the golden fruits are not ripe. This is not so. In fact, the golden fruits usually taste better than the red ones, although some of us find them all rather disappointing. Virtually all of the populations we have seen are polymorphic, but no data seem to be available on the frequencies of the forms within populations or whether the frequencies vary in different geographical areas. Nor is there any evidence as to how the polymorphism is maintained or whether it has any adaptive significance.

The salmonberry is closely related to the cultivated red raspberry, *Rubus idaeus,* and the two species have been successfully hybridized. Recessive genes for golden fruits are found in the red raspberry, and golden-fruited cultivated varieties exist, although they do not seem to be very popular. Several common red-fruited cultivated varieties have been shown to be heterozygous for fruit color. The gold-fruit allele is not nearly as common in the raspberry as in salmonberry, however.

Red and White Baneberry

Actaea rubra   (Ait.) Willd.   Ranunculaceae

Most baneberries seem to have red fruits, but white-fruited plants (Figure 3.34) also seem to be present in most populations throughout the wide range of this species. No data are available on the frequencies of the forms in populations or on the genetics of the polymorphism, but it is a good guess that fruit color is controlled by a single gene, with red dominant.

Figure 3.34 Red- and white-fruited forms of baneberry.

CHAPTER FOUR

POLYMORPHISMS OF THE BREEDING SYSTEM

Polymorphisms involving different mating types or different sexes represent a special kind of polymorphism. Most vertebrate animals have separate, genetically determined male and female individuals, and populations thus must maintain both sexes in order to reproduce and persist. More generally, when different morphs (or sexes) mate with the opposite morph preferentially or exclusively, the mating system is called *disassortative mating* or *negative assortative mating*. Disassortative mating will always maintain both morphs in the population.

In most species of flowering plants, each flower produces both pollen and ovules. Thus, in these species separate sexes analogous to those of animals do not exist. These species are called hermaphroditic. Some species do produce separate staminate (pollen-producing) and pistillate (ovule- and seed-producing) flowers, but both kinds of flowers are found on all the individuals in the population. This condition is called *monoecism* or *monoecy*. It is not a polymorphism, since all individuals are alike in bearing both staminate and pistillate flowers.

Examples of monoecious plants in British Columbia include many tree species, such as alder, garry oak, birches, and all the conifers except yews and junipers. The true sedges

(*Carex*) are all monoecious. All of these monoecious plants are pollinated by wind, and monoecism seems to be especially common in wind-pollinated plants in general. However, some insect-pollinated plants are monoecious, including cultivated begonias and most melons, squashes, and cucumbers. Oregon manroot, *Marah oreganus* (T. & G.) Howell, is a monoecious member of the cucumber family found in southwestern British Columbia that is pollinated by insects (Figure 4.1).

DIOECY

Dioecious plants have staminate (male) and pistillate (female) flowers on separate individual plants. Pollen from male plants must reach the pistil of female plants for seed to be produced, so the plants are obligately cross-pollinated. Since both sexes must be present for the population to reproduce sexually, the polymorphism is automatically retained in the population.

Dioecy is relatively rare in plants. Fewer than 5 percent of all flowering plants are dioecious, but the proportion is much higher on oceanic islands and among tropical forest trees.

In a few plants, such as white campion (*Silene alba*), sex expression is controlled by distinctive sex chromosomes, just as in humans and other mammals. The staminate plant has one X and one Y chromosome, and the pistillate plant has two Xs. The male is called the *heterogametic sex,* meaning that it is heterozygous for sex chromosomes, and half the pollen produced contains an X chromosome and half contains a Y chromosome. The female, known as the *homogametic sex,* is homozygous for sex chromosomes, so all eggs produced contain X chromosomes. In white campion the Y chromosome is much larger than the X chromosome, while in humans the reverse is true.

Most dioecious plants do not have cytologically distinguishable sex chromosomes. Instead, sex is usually con-

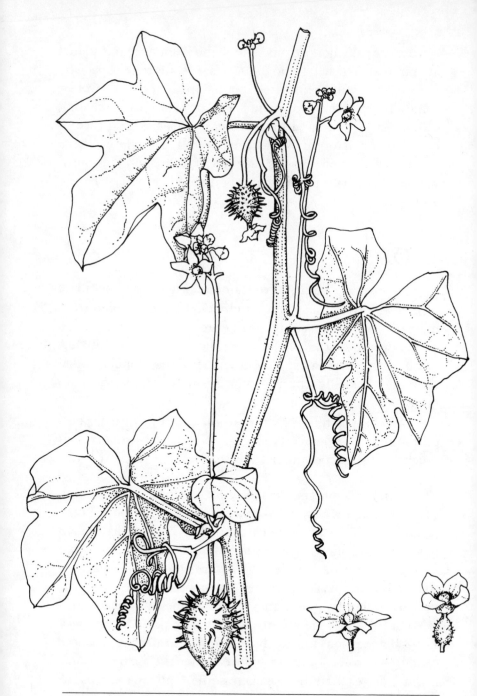

Figure 4.1   Oregon manroot, a monoecious plant, showing separate staminate and pistillate flowers. Pistillate flowers are less numerous and have a prominent ovary below the petals.

trolled by a single gene with two alleles. In some cases there is genetic evidence that the sex "gene" is really a complex composed of two separate genes, very close together on the chromosome, that are almost always inherited together as one unit. The male complex is actually composed of a gene for female sterility closely linked with a gene for male fertility, while the female complex has a gene for female fertility linked with a gene for male sterility. In most dioecious plants having genetic control of sex expression, the male plants are heterogametic and the females are homogametic. In a few cases, such as dioecious strawberries, the reverse is true. The beach strawberry, *Fragaria chiloensis* (L.) Duchesne, is a dioecious species of strawberry restricted to coastal sand dunes and is one of the parents of the cultivated strawberry, which is a complex hybrid derived from crosses between several species. Cultivated strawberries, however, have been selected for hermaphroditic flowers and are not dioecious, since it is not profitable to grow staminate plants that do not produce fruit.

White Campion or White Cockle

Silene alba (P. Mill.) Krause (synonyms: *Lychnis alba*, *Melandrium album*) Caryophyllaceae

White campion is a weed in British Columbia that was introduced from Europe. Most species of campion, including native ones, are hermaphroditic, each flower bearing both male and female parts. Thus, white campion must have evolved from a hermaphroditic ancestor by loss of the stamens in some plants and loss of the pistils in others. It exhibits a relatively advanced stage of dioecy, however, since it has strongly differentiated sex chromosomes. There are no vestiges of stamens in pistillate flowers nor of pistils in staminate flowers (Figure 4.2).

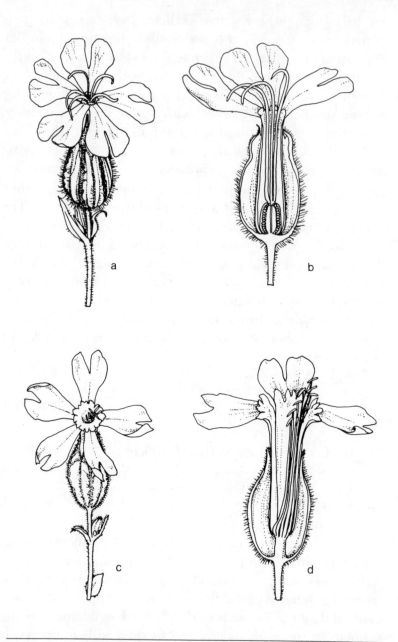

Figure 4.2   Separate sexes of white campion. (*a*) Female flower. (*b*) Vertical section through a female flower showing several protruding stigmas and ovary filled with ovules. (*c*) Male flower. (*d*) Vertical section through a male flower, showing stamens.

Half the pollen produced by male plants contains an X chromosome, and half contains a Y chromosome. Since females are homozygous for X chromosomes, all eggs contain only X chromosomes. Therefore, in crosses between males and females, half the progeny should be male and half should be female. In fact, in studies of sex ratios of plants in various areas of the world, a slight excess of female plants is found. One postulated explanation is that the pollen tubes of pollen grains carrying the larger Y chromosome, which produces males, grow more slowly in the female styles than the pollen tubes of pollen grains carrying the X chromosome.

Wild Blackberry

Rubus ursinus   Cham. & Schlecht.   var. *macropetalus*
  (Dougl.) Brown   Rosaceae

British Columbia's native wild blackberry is a low, trailing plant with small but delicious berries. It occurs only in the southwestern coastal part of the province and is particularly common on recently logged or burned land. The larger wild blackberries in the province, the evergreen blackberry (*Rubus laciniata*) and the Himalaya blackberry (*Rubus discolor;* synonym: *R. procerus*) are introduced from Europe and are not dioecious. There is another dioecious species of *Rubus* in British Columbia, the cloudberry (*Rubus chamaemorus* L.).

The staminate flowers of wild blackberry have fertile stamens and rudimentary but fairly conspicuous sterile pistils. Pistillate flowers have fertile pistils and sterile stamens. The most conspicuous difference between male and female flowers is size (Figure 4.3). Staminate flowers have petals that are about 50 percent longer and narrower than those of pistillate flowers. The staminate flowers are therefore much more conspicuous. Since staminate plants do not produce fruit, the blackberry patches with the biggest flowers produce the fewest berries.

Figure 4.3 Separate sexes of wild blackberry. The larger male is on the left, and the female is on the right. Note that the female has stigmas and the male stamens.

Osoberry, Indian Plum, or Skunkbush

Oemleria cerasiformis (Hook. & Arnott) Landon
  (synonym: *Osmaronia cerasiformis*)   Rosaceae

The osoberry is one of British Columbia's earliest flowering shrubs, but it is found only in the southwestern corner of the province. It is expecially common near Victoria. Its rank-smelling flowers are pollinated largely by March flies.

Osoberry is a distinctive plant found only on the Pacific Coast of North America, but it is closely related to the genus *Prunus*, which includes plums, cherries, peaches, and the other stone fruits. *Oemleria* differs from *Prunus* in having five pistils per flower instead of one and in being dioecious instead of hermaphroditic. Very rarely, however, osoberry plants with hermaphroditic flowers may be found. We have never seen such a plant in British Columbia, but we have seen one in California. Pistillate flowers may be easily mistaken for hermaphrodites, since pistillate flowers do have stamens. They are small, however, with nonfunctional anthers that

146

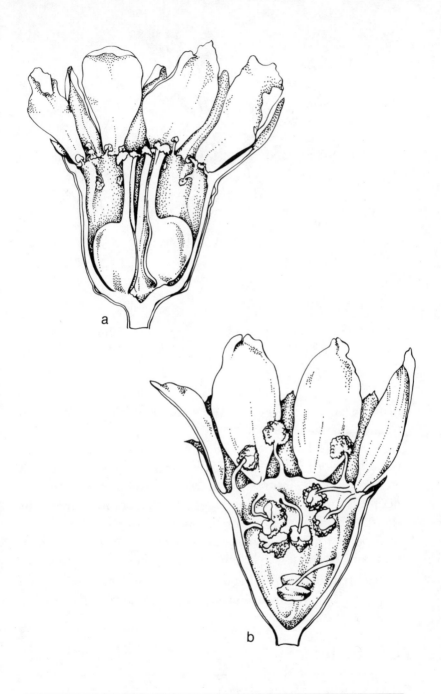

Figure 4.4　Separate sexes of osoberry. (*a*) Female. (*b*) Male. Note that the female has a ring of sterile vestigial stamens.

Figure 4.5   Separate sexes of goatsbeard. (*a*) Habit of plant. (*b*) Flower from a female plant. (*c*) Flower from a male plant.

produce no pollen (Figure 4.4). Staminate flowers show no trace of pistils.

There have been no thorough studies of the sexes in populations of osoberry, but there are indications that such studies might be interesting. Cursory observations by several people suggest that either males flower before females or there are more males in populations than there are females. In one population we looked at, however, there were equal numbers of males and females and they were randomly distributed. It has also been suggested that the rare hermaphroditic form is more common in the southern part of the range of the species.

Goatsbeard

Aruncus dioicus   (Walter) Fernald   Rosaceae

Goatsbeard is a large perennial herb that is particularly

148

Figure 4.6   Separate sexes of a species of willow. Female catkins are on the left and males on the right. (The small dark tips on the female flowers are the stigmas.)

common along partly shaded stream banks and road cuts. The large panicles of small flowers are attractive and conspicuous despite their small petals. The difference between the sexes is especially conspicuous at the end of flowering when the fruits are developing on the females and the male flowers are starting to wither, as shown in Color Plate 28 and Figure 4.5.

Willow

Salix species   Salicaceae

Like poplars and cottonwoods, the only other members of the family Salicaceae, all willows are dioecious. The flowers of willows, which are aggregated into catkins (Figure 4.6), are so simplified that they consist of only a hairy scale and either a pistil or stamens. The catkins of staminate trees fall off shortly after pollen is shed, while those on pistillate trees remain until the fruits are ripe and seed has been shed. In many cases dioecious plants have evolved from hermaphroditic ancestors, and sometimes rudimentary organs of the opposite sex are present. In plants like willows, which have such simplified flowers and have no hermaphroditic relatives, it is impossible to determine whether or not they evolved from hermaphroditic ancestors. Many botanists used to believe that all dioecious flowering plants had hermaphroditic ancestors, but recent studies of fossil flowers suggest that at least some dioecious plants may have been primitively dioecious.

GYNODIOECY

Gynodioecy refers to the situation in which some plants in a population have hermaphroditic flowers and other plants have only pistillate flowers. The frequency of pistillate plants can range from a few percent to nearly one-half (in which case the population may be functionally dioecious). Gynodioecy is a very rare breeding system, although in New Zealand it is more common; approximately 2 percent of all species there are gynodioecious.

In a gynodioecious population hermaphrodites contribute their genes to the next generation through both eggs and pollen, but pistillate plants contribute genes only through eggs. This amounts to selection against pistillate plants, so that for pistillate plants to be maintained in populations there must be some counteracting selection in their favor. It appears that selection in their favor is achieved in two ways. In some cases pistillate plants produce more flowers and seeds than do hermaphrodites. In other cases the progeny of pistillate plants may be better able to survive than the progeny of hermaphrodites. The reason for this is that the progeny of all pistillate plants result from cross-fertilization, while some of the progeny of hermaphrodites can result from self-fertilization. Self-fertilization often results in reduced vigor or viability because the progeny may be homozygous for recessive deleterious or lethal genes, a phenomenon known as *inbreeding depression*. Cross-fertilized progeny are less likely to be homozygous for deleterious recessive genes.

The pistillate condition, which is essentially male sterility, can be caused by a single recessive gene, by a dominant gene, or by more than one gene. In other cases the male sterility is caused by cytoplasmic rather than nuclear genes—probably by genes in the mitochondria. Cytoplasmic male sterility is inherited only through the egg and hence can only be inherited from the female parent. All progeny born on a cytoplasmic male-sterile (pistillate) plant inherit male-sterile cytoplasm. In cytoplasmic male-sterile plants there may be nuclear genes that can restore fertility, so that plants with male-sterile cytoplasm may be phenotypically hermaphroditic. The genetics of such systems can be quite complicated but are of great practical importance in producing hybrid seed of crop plants on a large scale, such as seed of hybrid corn, hybrid sorghum, and hybrid onions.

Northern Valerian

Valeriana dioica L. ssp. *sylvatica* (Soland.) F.G. Meyer
  Valerianaceae

Scouler's Valerian

Valeriana scouleri Rydb. Valerianaceae

Despite its scientific name, northern valerian is gynodioecious rather than dioecious (Figure 4.7). Northern valerian occurs in southeastern British Columbia as well as across Canada and in northern Europe. The populations of Scouler's valerian that we have seen are also gynodioecious, although gynodioecy has not previously been reported in this species. Scouler's valerian occurs in coastal British Columbia but is closely related to the Sitka valerian, *Valeriana sitchensis,*

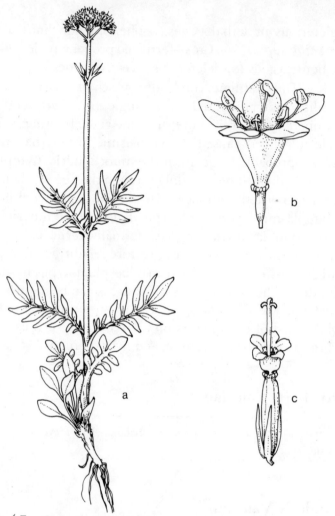

Figure 4.7 Gynodioecy in northern valerian. (*a*) Plant habit. (*b*) Hermaphrodite flower. (*c*) Pistillate, or female, flower.

common in subalpine meadows. In fact, some botanists regard Scouler's valerian as a variety of Sitka valerian. Sitka valerian always has hermaphroditic flowers, however, so it may be that the difference in breeding system is a previously unrecognized character separating the two species. Only observations of more populations of Scouler's valerian will tell.

The flowers of pistillate and hermaphroditic plants of valerian are conspicuously different in size, the pistillate flowers being only half as large as hermaphroditic flowers, as well as lacking fertile stamens. The genetics of gynodioecy in valerian has not been studied; nor are there any data on the frequency of pistillate plants in different populations.

HETEROSTYLY

Heterostyly is the name given to a floral polymorphism in which the flower forms differ in style and stamen lengths. It is one of the most unusual breeding systems in plants and is fairly rare. In British Columbia there are only three or four native heterostylous species and one naturalized species introduced from Europe. There are two kinds of heterostyly—distyly and tristyly.

In distylous plants, populations consist of two types of plants. One morph bears flowers with long styles and short stamens and is called the long-styled, or *pin,* form. The other morph bears flowers with short styles and long stamens and is called the short-styled, or *thrum,* form. The terms *pin* and *thrum* have a quaint derivation. Many years ago English florists referred to long-styled primroses, which displayed the globular stigma at the mouth of the corolla tube, as pin-eyed. Short-styled flowers, which displayed the anthers, were called thrum-eyed. *Thrum* was a term for the ends of weaver's threads, and the cluster of anthers apparently reminded some primrose-growing weavers, or weaving primrose growers, of such threads. Both forms of flowers produce fertile pollen and seeds. The plants are self-incompatible, however, so that if a flower is pollinated with pollen from the same plant, fertilization does not occur. Pollinations between plants of the same form are also incompatible and do not lead to fertilization, so that only pollinations between pins and thrums (in both directions) produce seed.

The two floral morphs of distylous plants are controlled by a single gene with two alleles. In most, the thrum form is dominant to pin, thrums having genotype Ss and pins ss. Since thrums usually cannot self-fertilize or cross with other thrums, homozygous dominant thrums do not occur. Crosses between the two forms give a 1:1 ratio of thrums and pins in the progeny, no matter whether pins or thrums are the female parent, since each must be fertilized by pollen from the opposite form. A few distylous species are self-compatible, and here homozygous thrums do occur.

The gene controlling distyly is actually another example of a gene complex composed of two or more tightly linked genes that are normally inherited together as a single unit. One part of the gene complex determines style length and compatibility and the other controls stamen length and pollen compatibility.

Distylous flowers usually differ in other features besides style and stamen length. In most cases, the thrum form produces larger pollen grains but fewer grains per flower, and the papillae, or bumps, on the stigmas of thrum flowers are usually smaller than those on pin stigmas.

The self-incompatibility system in distylous flowers means that the flowers are cross-fertilized. Only pollen from half the plants in a distylous population is compatible on a particular stigma, however, since pollinations between plants of the same form are also incompatible. The reciprocal differences in style and stamen length improve the chances that compatible pollen will be deposited on the stigma. For example, the part of an insect that is most likely to come in contact with anthers on long stamens is most likely to touch the stigma of a long style, while the part of the insect touching short stamens is most likely to touch short styles. Thus, pollen is preferentially transferred between the two forms.

Tristylous species have three floral morphs instead of two, as in distyly. Long-styled flowers have a long style and two sets of stamens, one short and one of middle length. Mid-styled flowers have mid-length styles and short and long stamens. Short-styled flowers have a short style and mid-length and long stamens. The three floral morphs are always on separate plants.

The pollen from a particular stamen length is compatible only with styles of that length. For example, pollen from long stamens in flowers having mid-length and short

154

styles is compatible with long styles and so will fertilize long-styled flowers. Therefore, each form is self-incompatible but can fertilize the other two if pollen from the appropriate set of stamens is deposited on the stigmas. The reciprocal placement of stamens and styles is thought to increase the efficiency of compatible pollination, just as it does in distylous plants.

Tristyly is controlled by the interaction of two genes, called S and M, each with two alleles. The dominant allele of the S gene makes the plants short styled, no matter which alleles are present at the M gene. If plants are homozygous recessive ss, they are non-short styled. They are mid styled if they have the dominant allele of the M gene. If they are homozygous recessive for both genes, they are long styled. The chart below summarizes the genetic constitution of the three morphs.

Short Styled	Mid Styled	Long Styled
$SsMM$	$ssMM$	$ssmm$
$SsMm$	$ssMm$	
$Ssmm$		

SS homozygotes do not occur because they could result only from crosses between short-styled plants, which of course are incompatible with each other.

Deer Cabbage

Fauria crista-galli (Menz. ex Hook) Makino
(synonym: *Nephrophyllidium crista-galli*) Menyanthaceae

Deer cabbage (Color Plate 29) is a distylous plant found in bogs and wet areas in coastal British Columbia, ranging from sea level to over 1000 m in altitude in the Coast Mountains in West Vancouver. It also occurs in Alaska and Japan and, rarely, on the Olympic Peninsula in Washington.

Figure 4.8   Heterostyly in deer cabbage. (*a*) The long-style shorter-stamen pin morph. (*b*) The reciprocal thrum. (*c*) The habit of the plant.

The flowers show the reciprocal arrangement of styles and stamens typical of distylous plants (Figure 4.8). The flowers have a sweet-fetid odor, something like the smell of a dirty garbage can sprayed with cheap perfume, which attracts a variety of pollinators but mostly flies. The petals have frilly edges and an erect, frilly flap down the center; such frilly flower parts are supposedly characteristic of fly-pollinated flowers. Although deer cabbage has been reported to be self-compatible, experiments with plants from West Vancouver have shown that they are self-incompatible. The confusion may have resulted from the fact that the fruits are partheno-carpic, meaning that the fruits will develop and ripen even if they are not pollinated, but they will be seedless. Bananas and pineapples are parthenocarpic.

Bogbean or Buckbean

Menyanthes trifoliata L. Menyanthaceae

Bogbean (Color Plates 30 and 31 and Figure 4.9) is related to deer cabbage but is more widespread, occurring in bogs, ponds, lakes, and rivers throughout most of northern America and Europe. The petals of the flowers are densely covered with fuzzy white hairs and do not have the fetid odor of deer cabbage. In British Columbia they seem to be pollinated mostly by bumblebees. Both deer cabbage and bogbean can reproduce vegetatively by rhizomes, and thus large patches of plants of the same floral form may be found. As a result, populations may not always contain the 1:1 ratio of pins and thrums expected in distylous plants.

Mistassini Primrose

Primula mistassinica Michx. Primulaceae

Mistassini primrose is an early spring flower found in the Rocky Mountains of southeastern British Columbia, as

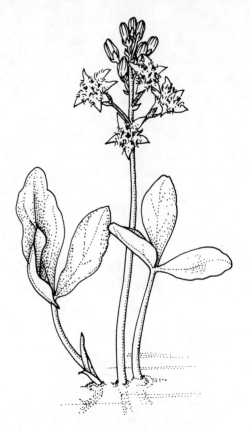

Figure 4.9   The habit of the bogbean plant.

well as north to the Yukon and east across Canada. It is the only common primrose native to British Columbia that is distylous. (The Siberian primrose, *P. sibirica* Jacq., has been found once near Atlin in far northwestern British Columbia and is also distylous.) Nearly all of the primroses cultivated in gardens are distylous.

British Columbia's other native primroses are homostylous. In homostylous primroses, the styles and stamens are the same length, and thus the anthers and stigma are at the same height in the flower. Figure 4.10 shows the pin and thrum forms of a distylous primrose and a long-homostyle primrose flower.

Such homostylous primroses have originated by chromosome exchange within the heterostyly gene complex in a

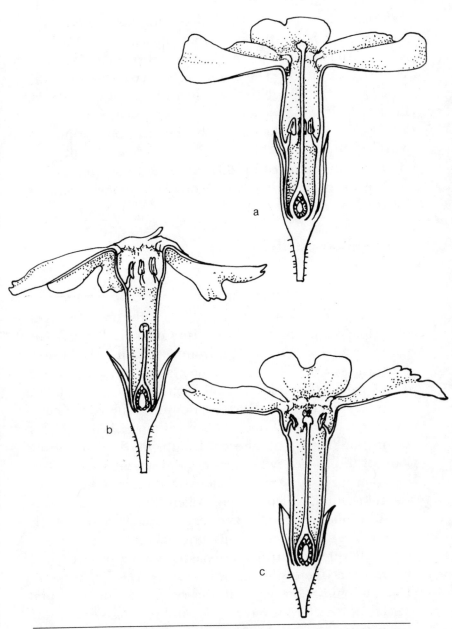

Figure 4.10 Heterostyly and homostyly in primroses. (*a*) Pin form,
(*b*) thrum form, and (*c*) a long homostyle, combining the
style length of a pin with the stamen length of a thrum.

heterozygous thrum. This kind of exchange between the two parts of a thrum allele (the parts for long stamens and short styles) and the two parts of a pin allele (for short stamens and long styles) can give two new types of alleles—one for long stamens and long styles and one for short stamens and short styles (Figure 4.11). These homostyles have combined the styles of one morph with the stamens from the other form. Because their anthers and stigmas are in close proximity, they are usually self-pollinating. The homostylous primroses native to British Columbia are all long homostyles. Because they are self-pollinated and do not need to attract insects, it is not surprising that they have evolved small, inconspicuous flowers.

Purple Loosestrife

Lythrum salicaria L. Lythraceae

Purple loosestrife (Figure 4.12) is the only tristylous plant found growing wild in British Columbia, but it is not native, having been introduced from Europe. It is established primarily in wet places, such as the Fraser River delta. It also occurs around the ponds in Jericho Park in Vancouver. It has tall spikes of magenta to purplish flowers in late summer and somewhat resembles fireweed from a distance. As in distylous plants, the stamens of different lengths in tristylous purple loosestrife produce pollen grains of different sizes and in different amounts. In purple loosestrife there is a difference in the color of the pollen as well. Pollen from long stamens is green, while pollen from mid-length and short stamens is yellow. The significance of this difference is not known.

Purple loosestrife is the classic example of a tristylous plant and was thoroughly studied by Charles Darwin. Although Darwin is most famous for his theory of evolution by natural selection, he wrote several books on breeding systems and pollination of plants. In his autobiography he wrote that, of his many studies, none had given him as much pleasure as his investigations of the mating systems of heterostylous plants.

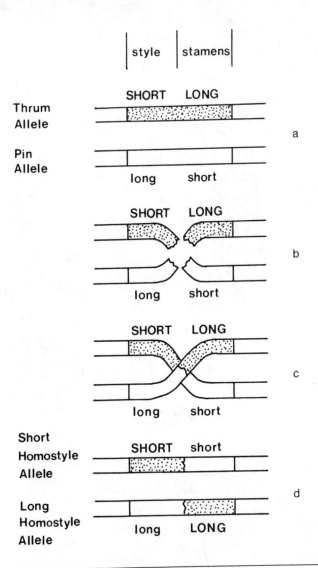

Figure 4.11 How chromosome exchange produces homostyle alleles.

(a) Thrum plants are heterozygous for one thrum and one pin allele.

(b) During egg or sperm formation, chromosomes are paired up next to each other and sometimes opposite breaks occur.

(c) They reconnect, but the ends sometimes connect with the other chromosome.

(d) This exchange between the two parts of the thrum and pin alleles gives two new alleles, each with styles and stamens of the same length.

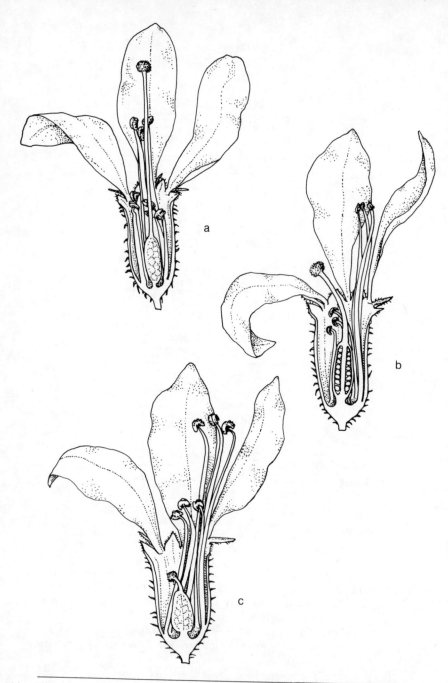

Figure 4.12 Tristyly in purple loosestrife. (*a*) Long, (*b*) mid, and (*c*) short style types are shown in longitudinal section. Note the complementary stamen lengths in each type.

CHAPTER FIVE

FORMATION OF SPECIES

Until now we have been primarily concerned with genetic variation within populations rather than genetic differences between populations. In order for similar populations to differentiate, or become genetically different, however, genetic variation must exist within at least one of the populations. Genetic polymorphism in the broad sense is the raw material for evolutionary change within a population and is therefore necessary for populations to become different from each other, or *diverge*.

DIVERGENCE

Populations diverge when the allele frequencies in the populations become different from each other, either by natural selection or by accident, which is known as *genetic drift*. As different alleles become fixed at more and more genes, the populations become more dissimilar genetically. This is the mechanism by which the different kinds of plants and animals have evolved. Usually it is a gradual process; thus, as one might expect, various degrees of difference can be found between populations that are in different stages of divergence.

An early stage of divergence may involve the fixation

of different alleles of the same gene in different populations, sometimes without any apparent geographical pattern. The white-flowered morph of midget phlox, which is fixed in a population on the south side of Sumas Mountain, is an example. So are the monomorphic winged and wingless fruited populations of the small-flowered sea blush, although in this case the distribution of populations on Vancouver Island does show a geographical pattern.

Blue-eyed Mary

Collinsia parviflora   Dougl. ex Lindl.   Scrophulariaceae

     Careful comparisons of different populations of the same species often reveal subtle differences in genetically controlled characters. If seeds from different populations of blue-eyed Mary are grown together in the same environment so that variation caused by ecological factors is controlled, numerous differences among the populations are apparent. Differences in flower size have already been mentioned in Chapter 1. Frequency differences for the leaf-spot gene have been illustrated in Chapter 3; in addition, the shape and size of leaf spots consistently differ among populations. Figure 5.1 shows the range of spot shapes seen on plants from some different populations. Populations of *Collinsia* plants may also differ in leaf shape, size of the teeth on the leaves, and amount and color of pigmentation (other than the spots). Plants from different populations grown under uniform conditions in a growth chamber show these differences in a striking way. These populations illustrate an early stage of genetic differentiation from each other. This pattern of evolutionary diversification results from a combination of natural selection and accidental fixation of genes in different populations.

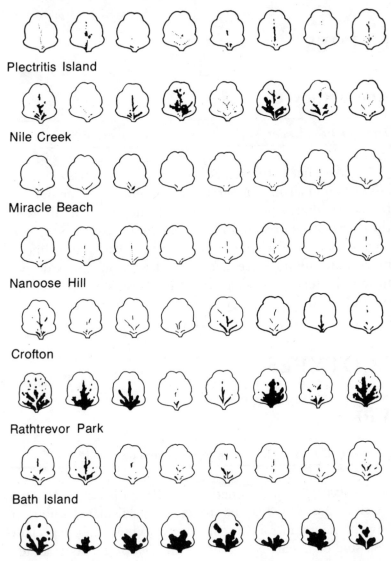

Plectritis Island

Nile Creek

Miracle Beach

Nanoose Hill

Crofton

Rathtrevor Park

Bath Island

Little River

Figure 5.1   Interpopulation differences of leaf spots in blue-eyed Mary. Each row shows a representative leaf from eight plants collected in one of eight different localities in British Columbia.

CLINES

Annual Clover

Trifolium tridentatum   Lindl.   Fabaceae (Leguminosae)

Another pattern of geographical variation is a cline. A *cline* is a gradual directional change in some character, or in its frequency, that is correlated with distance. On a small scale, the distribution of spotted leaves in annual clover on Carlos Island is a good example of a cline. In this case it is a cline in morph and in allele frequency. By definition, clines do not have to be related to selective differences along an environmental gradient, but they often are—as in the case of the clover on Carlos Island. (See Figure 3.6.)

ECOTYPES

Yarrow

Achillea millefolium   L.   Asteraceae (Compositae)

Ecotypes are genetically differentiated races of a species that are adapted to some particular habitat or environmental factor. Climatic ecotypes have been especially well studied in yarrow, *Achillea millefolium* L. (Asteraceae), which grows under a wide range of climatic conditions (Figure 2.12). Seacoast populations are genetically differentiated from populations growing at timberline in the mountains. The important differences are genetically controlled physiological differences that allow the plants to survive and reproduce in habitats that differ markedly in temperature, growing season, and other environmental variables. In addition, morphological differences, such as size and hairiness, which may also be adaptive, can distinguish ecotypes, although in some cases there are no easily observed morphological differences. In either case, the adaptive differences are genetically controlled and not environmentally induced, and plants of different ecotypes maintain their differences even when grown together under uniform conditions.

Yellow Monkey Flower

Mimulus guttatus   DC.   Scrophulariaceae

A possible example of an ecotype is a small form of yellow monkey flower, called variety *depauperatus* (Figure 5.2). Hitchcock and Cronquist's *Flora* notes that it occurs in less wet habitats than the more robust variety *guttatus*. However, we have observed the small form on Nanoose Hill and Mill Hill near Victoria growing together with the large. The small form flowers much earlier than most of the large plants on Nanoose Hill. We have tried crossing the two varieties but with no luck, so they could be different species.

SUBSPECIES

Distance or topographic barriers may severely restrict gene exchange between populations, allowing divergence to proceed. Populations or groups of populations that differ from each other in genetically controlled characters and that exhibit different geographical ranges are sometimes called geographical races. If the morphological differences are conspicuous and fairly constant, these races may be named taxonomically as different varieties or subspecies of the same species. Different subspecies (or varieties—they are the same thing genetically) are still able to interbreed where their ranges come together, and they may show a spectrum of intermediate forms. Genetic divergence and isolation is not complete between subspecies.

167

Figure 5.2   Yellow monkey flowers. (a) *Mimulus guttatus* var. *depauperatus* and (b) *Mimulus guttatus* var. *guttatus*.

Foamflower

Tiarella trifoliata L.   Saxifragaceae

Foamflower has a geographically restricted polymorphism in leaf shape as well as an ecologically and geographically distinctive subspecies that differs in leaf shape. It therefore shows two different stages in geographical differentiation.

Foamflower is a common forest herb in southern and coastal British Columbia. *Tiarella trifoliata* ssp. *trifoliata* has compound leaves with three definite leaflets, while *T. trifoliata* ssp. *unifoliata* has simple but three-lobed leaves (Figure 5.3). The two subspecies differ in ecological preferences as well. Subspecies *trifoliata* occurs from sea level to an elevation of about 900 m while subspecies *unifoliata* usually occurs above this altitude. Subspecies *unifoliata* also occurs farther east in the mountains of the southern interior of British Columbia. The range of subspecies *unifoliata* extends farther south, into California, while subspecies *trifoliata* occurs farther north, into coastal Alaska (Figure 5.4) Where the two subspecies occur together—for example, at about 900m in altitude on Mt. Seymour in North Vancouver—they hybridize and show a range of intermediate forms. Here plants can be found that have both simple and compound leaves and simple but very deeply lobed leaves (Figure 5.5).

Populations of *Tiarella trifoliata* ssp. *trifoliata* on southern Vancouver Island, as well as on the Gulf and San Juan islands, and occasionally on the Lower Mainland—for example, at Lighthouse Park in West Vancouver—are polymorphic for leaf shape. Some plants in these populations are typical *Tiarella trifoliata* ssp.*trifoliata,* but others have finely dissected leaves (Figure 5.3). The plants with finely dissected leaves have been called *Tiarella trifoliata* var. *laciniata*. As far as we have observed, however, the *laciniata* plants never occur in discrete populations of their own but only with typical plants of subspecies *trifoliata*. Populations with *laciniata*

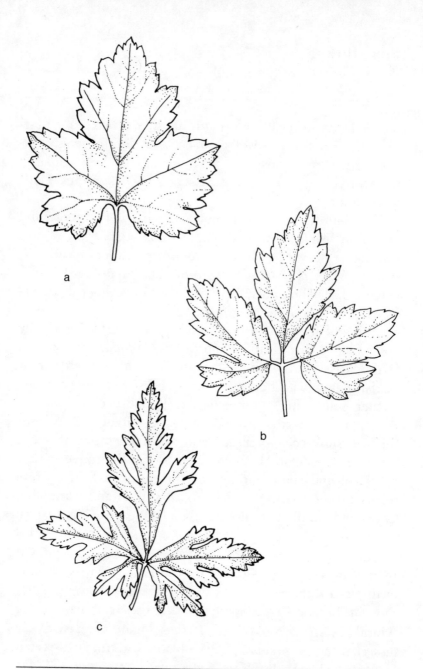

Figure 5.3   Subspecies and varieties of foamflower *Tiarella trifoliata*.
(*a*) *T. trifoliata* subspecies *unifoliata*. (*b*) *T. trifoliata*
subspecies *trifoliata*. (*c*) *T. trifoliata* subspecies *trifoliata*
variety *laciniata*.

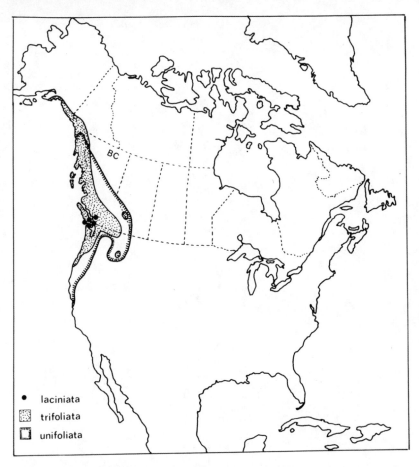

Figure 5.4 Distribution map of *Tiarella trifoliata* subspecies and variety.

plants are always polymorphic, and thus *laciniata* does not deserve taxonomic status as a variety or species.

No one has yet studied the genetics of this polymorphism. What is puzzling is why the *laciniata* form never seems to occur alone. If it is a heterozygote for a gene that is lethal when homozygous but selectively advantageous when heterozygous, that would explain its occurrence in only mixed populations. The situation may be more complicated, however, or perhaps the *laciniata* gene is a mutant that is in the process of replacing typical subspecies *trifoliata* in this region—a new subspecies in the process of evolving.

Figure 5.5   A hybrid between *Tiarella trifoliata* subspecies *trifoliata* and *Tiarella trifoliata* subspecies *unifoliata* from Mt. Seymour Provincial Park, North Vancouver. Note that the plant has both the leaf types of the presumed parents.

Figure 5.6　Douglas spiraea.

Douglas Spiraea or Hardhack

Spiraea douglasii　Hook.　Rosaceae

Our most common species of spiraea, *S. douglasii* (Figure 5.6), is found in wet places, along ditches, lakes, or swamps. Like many species that occur both on the coast and in the interior of the province, it is differentiated into a coastal and an interior variety. The coastal and interior plants were originally described as different species, but they are very similar, differing in only one obvious character—the underside of the leaves. The undersides of the leaves of the coastal plants, subspecies *douglasii*, are covered with short, densely matted woolly hairs that make the underside of the leaf conspicuously grayish. The undersides of the leaves of the interior plants, subspecies *menziesii* (Hook.) Calder & Taylor, lack hairs, and they appear light green (Figure 5.7). The genetics of hairiness in this species has not been studied, but presence or absence of hairs is likely controlled by only one or a few genes.

In river valleys that cut through the Cascades or Coast Mountains, the genes for hairless leaves have spread toward the coast. In these areas plants with either hairless or hairy leaves may be found, as well as intermediate plants with leaves only slightly hairy below. Leaves of these intermediate plants sometimes become less hairy with age, the remaining hairs being most abundant near the veins on the leaf. Hairless

173

Figure 5.7   Leaves of Douglas spiraea. Subspecies *douglasii* (*left*) is coastal and has woolly hairs on the undersides of its leaves, making them appear light gray in the photograph. The interior subspecies *menziesii* (*right*) has no hairs.

and intermediate plants extend to the coast in the Squamish River valley and down Howe Sound and occasionally even to Vancouver. Geographical isolation between the two subspecies is obviously not complete, and they have diverged evolutionarily only to a limited extent.

There are several other species in British Columbia a d the Pacific Northwest that have differentiated coastal and interior subspecies or varieties. Usually the Cascade Mountains are the topographic boundary between the two varieties. The distinctions between them may be less clear in the Fraser River valley and Columbia Gorge, where the western and eastern varieties hybridize and show intermediate forms. Some examples are listed in Table 5.1.

TABLE 5.1

Examples of Species with Differentiated
Coastal and Interior Varieties

Species	Coastal Variety	Interior Variety	Major Differences
Saskatoonberry *Amelanchier alnifolia* Nutt.	var. *semiintegrifolia* (Hook.) C.L. Hitchc.	var. *alnifolia*	petal length, plant habit
Camas *Camassia quamash* (Pursh) Greene	var. *maxima* (Gould) Boivin	var. *quamash*	flower color, petal width
Black hawthorn *Crateagus douglasii* Lindl.	var. *suksdorfii* Sarg.	var. *douglasii*	stamen number, leaf shape
Bitter cherry *Prunus emarginata* (Dougl. ex Hook.) Walp.	var. *mollis* (Dougl. ex Hook.) Brewer	var. *emarginata*	plant habit, pubescence
Douglas fir *Pseudotsuga menziesii* (Mirb.) Franco	var. *menziesii*	var. *glauca* (Beissner) Franco	cones, tree size
Nootka rose *Rosa nutkana* Presl	var. *nutkana*	var. *hispida* Fern.	teeth on leaves
Death camas *Zigadenus venenosus* Wats.	var. *venenosus*	var. *gramineus* (Rydb.) Walsh	leaf bases, sepals

ALLOPATRIC SPECIATION

As we have seen, geographically isolated populations of plants frequently become genetically different as a result of different selective pressures as well as chance events (genetic drift). If the degree of differentiation is small, or if it is incomplete and the populations hybridize and show intermediate forms where their ranges meet, they may be distinguished taxonomically as varieties or subspecies. Given enough time and different selective pressures, however, such geographically separate varieties may diverge to the point that they are genetically and morphologically distinct. This process may continue until they can no longer exchange genes (hybridize)—or at least they do not intergrade or merge into each other—and they become distinct species. This process of speciation by divergence in geographically isolated populations is called *allopatric speciation*. (*Allopatric* literally means "other place.")

As might be expected, the distinction between well-differentiated subspecies and poorly differentiated species is a matter of degree. Species may be genetically isolated from each other by a variety of means, some more complete than others. Adaptations to different pollinators may prevent crossing between two related species; so would different flowering times or the adaptation of two species to different habitats so that they do not occur together. Adaptation to different habitats may also keep the two species from intergrading because their intermediate hybrids would be eliminated by competition from the better-adapted parental species. In many cases physiological isolation evolves and pollen from different species will not germinate or grow on the stigma of another species, or, if it does, the sperm produced by each pollen grain cannot fuse with an egg of a different species. Species that can hybridize will also remain genetically distinct if their hybrids are weak, inviable, or sterile. When species have differentiated to the stage where they are genetically isolated from each other, they can occur with each other, or *sympatrically,* and still remain distinct.

Closely related allopatric species (species derived from each other or a common ancestor with geographically separated ranges) represent the next stage of genetic differentiation. The number of closely related allopatric species in British Columbia, however, is much smaller than in other parts of the world. Since British Columbia was almost completely glaciated as recently as twelve thousand years ago, there has not been enough time for a significant amount of speciation to take place. Our examples, in fact, are of species that also occur farther south, in the United States, where the speciation probably took place in unglaciated areas. A common pattern of distribution is for one species to be coastal and the other interior, especially since the Cascade Mountains provide a north-south topographic barrier that also produces drastically different climates on the east and west sides of the mountains. We will consider only one example of closely related allopatric species with a coastal and interior distribution pattern.

Pacific Ninebark

Physocarpus capitatus (Pursh) Kuntze   Rosaceae

Mallow Ninebark

Physocarpus malvaceus (Greene) Kuntze   Rosaceae

Ninebark is a woody shrub in the rose family that gets its name from its scaly bark, which builds up in several layers on older parts of the stem. There are not necessarily nine layers; in his journals of the Lewis and Clark Expedition to the Pacific Northwest in the early 1800s, William Clark referred to the plant as sevenbark. The coastal species, called Pacific ninebark, is distinguished by its larger size and larger leaves with sharp, pointed teeth and lobes, as well as by its flowers, which have four or five hairless pistils. The interior species, called mallow ninebark, found east of the Cascade Mountains,

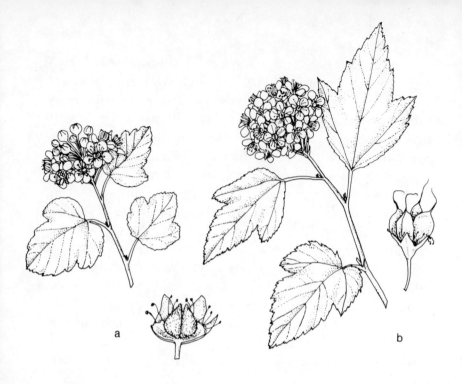

Figure 5.8   Allopatric species of ninebark. (*a*) Interior mallow ninebark and (*b*) coastal Pacific ninebark. Note the difference in size and number of pistils in the flower (seen in the inset fruits).

is smaller and has smaller leaves with rounded lobes and flowers that usually have only two or three hairy pistils (Figure 5.8). The two species are found only on opposite sides of the Cascades in Washington and Oregon, but in British Columbia Pacific ninebark also occasionally occurs in wetter forests in the southern interior. Because southern British Columbia is almost completely mountainous, wet forests occur farther east here than in the United States. In addition, the main track of rain-bearing storms runs eastward at about the forty-ninth parallel, so wet forests containing coastal species are able to extend farther inland in British Columbia. Thus, Pacific ninebark has extended its range so that it is partly sympatric with mallow ninebark at least geographically if not in local habitat.

a   b

Figure 5.9   Closely related species of sea blush. (*a*) *Plectritis congesta*
and (*b*) *Plectritis brachystemon*. The main differences are
associated with the flowers: *P. congesta* is a rich pink and
P. brachystemon is white; in addition, *P. congesta* has an
attractive and unforgettable scent.

In contrast to the ninebark species, the two species of
sea blush, *Plectritis congesta* and *P. brachystemon* (Figure
5.9), are examples of obviously related species that grow in
the same geographic locality and often in the same habitat,
intermixed or within centimeters of each other. Although
sharing many features in common, they cannot hybridize with
each other. Therefore, they can coexist sympatrically and
remain genetically separate.

HYBRIDS BETWEEN INTERFERTILE SPECIES

If closely related species are genetically isolated from each other by some mechanism other than physiological isolation, interspecific hybrids are possible. The two species must occur close enough to each other for pollination to take place, and the hybrids must be viable and competitive enough to become established. If the hybrids are fertile, crosses may occur between themselves or between them and the parental types, resulting in a variety of intermediate types. Populations showing a range of such intermediate types are called *hybrid swarms*.

Interspecific hybridization is rare in British Columbia compared to many parts of the world. Nevertheless, several cases of interspecific hybridization are known, and in a few cases the hybrids are fairly common in areas where both parent species occur together. Such interspecific hybrids usually combine the characteristics of their two parents and are often intermediate in appearance.

White Campion X Red Campion

Silene alba (P. Mill.) Krause x *Silene dioica* (L.) Clairv.
Caryophyllaceae

Red and white campion are both native to Europe, where they hybridize frequently when they grow together. White campion or white cockle is a widespread weed in southern Canada, but red campion is only rarely established, primarily in coastal British Columbia and a few areas of Atlantic Canada. The two species differ most conspicuously in flower color, white campion having white flowers and red campion having reddish purple flowers. The flower color is due to anthocyanin pigment and an anthoxanthin pigment

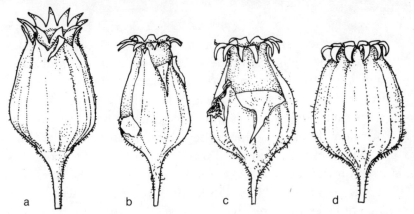

Figure 5.10 Seed capsules of white and red campion and their hybrids. (*a*) Seed capsule of white campion. (*b*) Seed capsule of a hybrid that had white campion as the female parent and red campion as the male parent. (*c*) Seed capsule of a hybrid that had red campion as the female parent and white campion as the male parent. (*d*) Seed capsule of red campion. Note that the hybrids resemble their female parents more than their male parents.

that causes a bluing of the anthocyanin. White campion has no anthocyanin in its flower petals but does have anthoxanthin, which is responsible for the creamy color of the underside of the petals. The species differ in several other characters. The calyx teeth of white campion are 4.8 to 6.5 mm long—more than twice as long as those of red campion. The capsule teeth are upright in white campion and rolled back in red campion, and the leaves of white campion are narrower.

Hybrids are intermediate in all these characters, but the pink petals are the most obvious indication of hybridity. In white campions the absence of anthocyanin pigment is due to a homozygous recessive gene, and in red campions the dark red color is due to a homozygous dominant gene. The red allele, however, is only partly dominant, and in one dose (the heterozygous condition) it can produce only a small amount of pigment; as a result, the flower is pink. There is also a certain amount of modifier gene action in the hybrid, which contributes to the incomplete expression of anthocyanin production.

Although hybrids are intermediate in length of calyx

teeth and leaf shape, and have reflexed but not rolled back calyx teeth (Figure 5.10), there is some difference in individual hybrid plants depending on which direction the original cross was made. Hybrids tend to resemble their female parent more than their male parent, showing some degree of maternal, presumably cytoplasmic, inheritance. Both species are dioecious, however, with well-differentiated sex chromosomes, and some of the difference could be due to sex-linked genes. In fact there are small but consistent differences between males and females in some characters, such as the length of calyx teeth, especially in white campion.

Yellow Columbine × Sitka Columbine

Aquilegia flavescens Wats. × *Aquilegia formosa* Fisch.
Ranunculaceae

Yellow columbine is found in southern British Columbia, northern Washington, and the Rocky Mountains from Alberta south to Utah and Colorado. Sitka columbine has red and yellow flowers and is widespread in western North America. The ranges of the two overlap, but they usually do not grow together since yellow columbine requires a more alpine habitat. The two species are completely interfertile, however, and in several areas they hybridize freely in nature (Color Plate 32 and Figure 5.11).

Flowers of the two species are probably adapted to different pollinators. Flowers of Sitka columbine have red sepals and red spurs on the petals, but the forward-pointing blades of the petals are yellow and rather short, usually 2 to 5 mm long, so that the stamens and pistils stick out from the flowers. They are adapted to pollination by hummingbirds, whose heads contact the stamens and pistils when they stick their bills into the nectar-bearing spurs. Hummingbird-pollinated flowers are often red or reddish, since hummingbirds can see red and are attracted to the color, while bees cannot see true red at all.

Figure 5.11 Hybridization in columbine. *Left:* a flower of Sitka columbine (red). *Right:* a flower of yellow columbine (yellow and smaller). *Center:* a flower of the hybrid, which is intermediate in color and shape of the central corolla "cones."

The flowers of yellow columbine are similar except that they are wholly yellow and the blades of the petals are longer, from 6 to 13 mm long, forming a loose cup around the stamens and pistils. Apparently the pollinators of yellow columbine have not been studied, but it is probably pollinated by bees or perhaps moths. Bee-pollinated flowers may be many colors, but they are not usually red, and moth-pollinated flowers are typically a pale color that shows up well at dusk. Adaptation to different pollinators is one way that genetic isolation is maintained between the two species; another is their usual preference for different habitats. Because the pollinators are not always constant to "their" species, however, hybridization can occur when the two species grow together.

Hybrids between the two species are almost exactly intermediate. Hybrid flowers have pinkish yellow sepals and spurs, and the blades of the petals are of intermediate length. Segregation in F_2 progeny and backcrosses to either of the parent species in hybrid swarms results in an array of plants

183

showing a complete range of intergradation between the two species.

Intermediate Manzanita

Arctostaphylos × *media*   Greene   Ericaceae
A hybrid of hairy manzanita (*Arctostaphylos columbiana* Piper)
and kinnikinnick (*Arctostaphylos uva-ursi* (L.) Sprengel)

Kinnikinnick, or bearberry (*A. uva-ursi*), is a low, trailing evergreen that is widespread in the province. Hairy manzanita (*A. columbiana*) is a tall shrub restricted to dry areas in southwestern coastal parts of the province, particularly southern Vancouver Island. The two species are interfertile and often hybridize if they occur together. The hybrids are intermediate in leaf shape, hairiness, and flower shape, but most conspicuously in height. The hybrids, named *Arctostaphylos* × *media,* are trailing shrubs with ascending branches reaching 30 cm or more in height; kinnikinnick usually grows tightly appressed to the ground (Figure 5.12). Species of *Arctostaphylos* are notorious for their ability to hybridize where they occur together. In California, where there are many species of *Arctostaphylos,* many different hybrid combinations have been found.

Hybrid Mountain Heather

Phyllodoce × *intermedia*   (Hook.) Camp   Ericaceae
A hybrid of red mountain heather (*Phyllodoce empetriformis*
(Sw.) D. Don) and cream mountain heather (*Phyllodoce glanduliflora*
(Hook.) Coville)

Flowers of the red and cream mountain heather differ in flower color, corolla shape, and presence of sticky glands. Red mountain heather has bright pink (not really red), open, bell-shaped flowers without sticky glandular hairs. Cream mountain heather has cream-colored flowers that are urn

184

Figure 5.12 Hybridization in *Arctostaphylos*. (*a*) Hairy manzanita
(inset shows a reduced larger branch showing plant
habit). (*b*) Kinnikinnick. (*c*) The hybrid. Note the
intermediate size and shape of the hybrid. It also lacks the
hairs of hairy manzanita.

shaped, with a small opening, and sticky glandular hairs. Where the two species occur together hybrids that are sparsely glandular and intermediate in flower color and shape are frequently found. Some plants of these hybrids are very attractive and have been brought into cultivation as named cultivated varieties that are vegetatively propagated (Figure 5.13).

Pyramid Spiraea: A Possible Hybrid Species

Spiraea pyramidata Greene   Rosaceae

Pyramid spiraea (Color Plate 33) is virtually an exact intermediate between Douglas spiraea, *Spiraea douglasii* Hook., and birch-leaved spiraea, *Spiraea betulifolia* Pallas ssp. *lucida* (Dougl. ex Greene) Taylor and Macbr. This has suggested to several botanists that pyramid spiraea originated as a hybrid between the other two species. Douglas spiraea has deep rose pink or magenta flowers with relatively short stamens and a narrow, cone-shaped inflorescence (Color Plate 34). Birch-leaved spiraea has white flowers with very long stamens and a flat-topped inflorescence (Color Plate 35). Pyramid spiraea has pink flowers, stamens that are intermediate in length, and a broad but pyramidal inflorescence. Leaf morphology in the three species is very similar.

Pyramid spiraea, however, is rather uniform in morphology and is widely distributed throughout British Columbia and the Pacific Northwest, occurring in places where neither parent is present. It therefore appears to be a genetically stable, self-perpetuating, genuine species. Apparently it has the same chromosome number as both parent species, so it is not an allopolyploid derivative of the other two. (See below for a description of the phenomenon of allopolyploidy.)

The origin of pyramid spiraea has not been studied; nor have there been any published attempts to synthesize the hybrid between Douglas spiraea and birch-leaved spiraea. The possibility remains that pyramid spiraea originated as a hybrid between the other two species and was subsequently

186

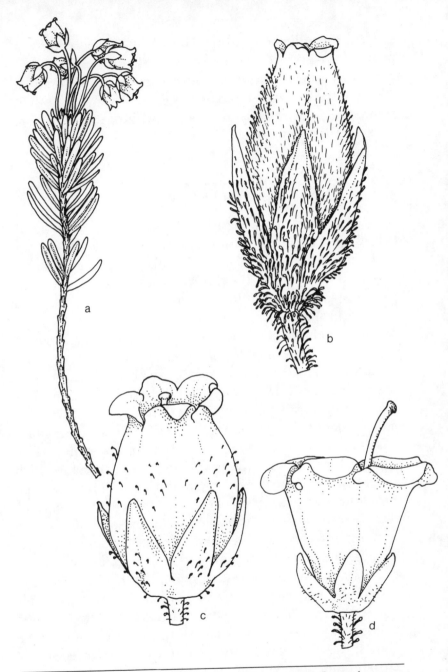

Figure 5.13 Hybridization in mountain heather. (*a*) General appearance of a hybrid heather branch. (*b*) Cream mountain heather. (*c*) Hybrid. (*d*) Red mountain heather. Again, note the intermediacy of the hybrid.

selected for uniformity so that invariant, self-perpetuating populations evolved and extended their range. The other possibility is that the three species originated from a common ancestor and diverged more or less equally from each other, resulting in a series of three species with one intermediate between the other two.

ALLOPOLYPLOIDY

In some cases related plant species are capable of hybridizing, but the resulting hybrids are sterile and cannot reproduce. Although hybrid sterility may have several causes, a frequent cause is that the chromosomes contributed by each parent species are so different that they do not pair and separate properly during sex cell formation. The resulting egg or pollen cells do not each have a complete single set of chromosomes, and egg or pollen cells having extra chromosomes or lacking chromosomes are usually inviable.

However, rarely, abnormal cell division in such hybrids (or in nonhybrids, for that matter) results in cells with a doubled set of chromosomes. If a sterile interspecific hybrid has by chance doubled the number of chromosomes in its cells, then each parent set is present in duplicate; therefore, each parent set has a partner to pair up with during sex cell formation and production of eggs and pollen cells is normal.

Such a hybrid with a doubled chromosome number has four sets of chromosomes and is called an *allotetraploid*. Because the two chromosome sets from each parent species can pair normally, the allotetraploid is fertile. It is also genetically isolated from its two parents, since they have only two sets of chromosomes. A hybrid between an allotetraploid and a diploid results in a plant with three sets of chromosomes; these triploid hybrids are sterile, since three sets of chromosomes cannot pair evenly.

Allopolyploidy, the occurrence of several sets of chromosomes of different origin, is actually very common in plants, and many species have originated in this way.

Allopolyploids have also been synthesized by botanists and plant breeders; the grain crop triticale is an allopolyploid synthesized from a sterile hybrid of wheat (*Triticum*) and rye (*Secale*) using a drug, colchicine, that can double chromosome numbers. Triticale is becoming increasingly cultivated in Canada and other countries. Triticale flour, bread, and biscuits are now available in supermarkets throughout Canada.

Allotetraploids are usually intermediate in appearance between their diploid parent species. They may or may not be intermediate in physiological or ecological characteristics, and they may expand their range into habitats or geographical areas not occupied by their parents. Unfortunately, the identification of new allopolyploids is not possible without a good research microscope, so amateurs can do little but observe already proven cases.

Western Bunchberry

Cornus unalaschkensis Ledeb. Cornaceae

Three species of bunchberries, dwarf herbaceous dogwoods, occur in western North America, and all three occur in British Columbia. They are very similar and not always easy to identify without using microscopic characters, but in British Columbia they have fairly distinct geographical ranges. By far the most common bunchberry in British Columbia, and the only one found in the southern half of the province west of the Rocky Mountains, is western bunchberry. It is a tetraploid and is morphologically intermediate between the two diploid species, Canada bunchberry, *Cornus canadensis* L., found from the Rocky Mountains eastward, and northern bunchberry, *Cornus suecica,* found in the northwesternmost part of coastal British Columbia and, more commonly, in Alaska.

Canada bunchberry is fairly easily recognized by its whorl of four to six leaves at the top of the stem and its greenish white flower petals. (Note: the four conspicuous

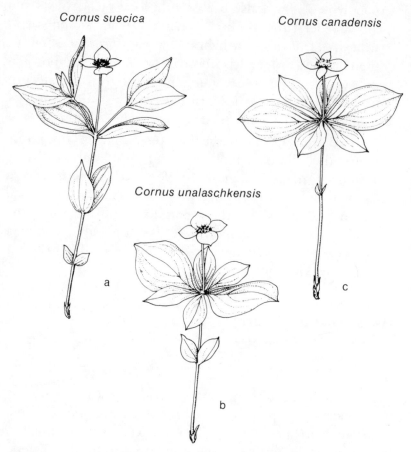

Figure 5.14 Allopolyploidy in bunchberry. (*a*) Northern bunchberry. (*b*) The allopolyploid, western bunchberry. (*c*) Canada bunchberry.

bracts or modified leaves that surround the flower clusters are not petals and are white in all three species.) Northern bunchberry usually has three to six more or less equal pairs of leaves along its short stem, although they are sometimes close together at the top of the stem and simulate a whorl of leaves. The petals of northern bunchberry are purple or at least partly purple. Western bunchberry has flowers like those of northern bunchberry but usually has whorls of leaves like those of Canada bunchberry (Figure 5.14).

The geographical range of western bunchberry is almost completely separate from its two parent species, being south of that of northern bunchberry and west and south of that of Canada bunchberry. However, the ranges of northern bunchberry and Canada bunchberry overlap north of the Alaska panhandle, and hybrids between these two species have been found there. These hybrids look like western bunchberry, but they are diploid (no chromosome doubling having occurred) and mostly sterile; only about half their pollen is viable, and they rarely set seed. Current hybridization between the two parent species takes place outside the present range of western bunchberry and apparently has not yet led to the production of allotetraploids there. The hybridization and allopolyploidy that produced western bunchberry took place sometime before the last glaciation, and the tetraploids survived farther south than the parent species and subsequently recolonized an area where the parents had not occurred or had been eliminated.

Kruckeberg's Sword Fern

Polystichum kruckebergii   Wagner   Aspleniaceae

Rock Shield Fern

Polystichum scopulinum   (D.C. Eat.) Maxon   Aspleniaceae

The sword ferns and holly ferns, *Polystichum,* are a large group of ferns widespread in western North America. Identification of the species is sometimes difficult, partly because the various diploid species hybridize readily when they grow together. The hybrids are usually completely sterile, but hybrids between various pairs of diploids have given rise to fertile tetraploid species. These allotetraploids are intermediate in appearance, although sometimes they have established wider geographical ranges than either of their parents.

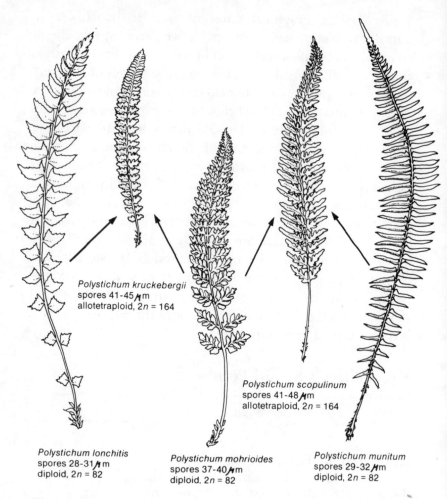

Polystichum kruckebergii
spores 41-45 μm
allotetraploid, 2n = 164

Polystichum scopulinum
spores 41-48 μm
allotetraploid, 2n = 164

Polystichum lonchitis
spores 28-31 μm
diploid, 2n = 82

Polystichum mohrioides
spores 37-40 μm
diploid, 2n = 82

Polystichum munitum
spores 29-32 μm
diploid, 2n = 82

Figure 5.15 Allopolyploidy in *Polystichum*. Kruckeberg's sword fern and rock shield fern are allopolyploids derived from hybrids of the species indicated.

Two rather similar species of *Polystichum* in British Columbia are allotetraploids. They are similar because one of the diploid parents is common to both of them. Both species are confined to rocky cliffs and taluses, especially on ultramafic rocks (rocks high in magnesium and iron and low in calcium). Rock shield fern is more widespread than Kruckeberg's sword fern, which is a rather rare fern.

192

Rock shield fern is an allotetraploid derived from a hybrid between *Polystichum munitum* (Kaulf.) Presl, the western sword fern common in low-elevation forests, and *Polystichum mohrioides* (Bory) Presl, the Shasta holly fern, a rather rare fern confined to rocky cliffs and taluses, mainly in the mountains. Kruckeberg's sword fern is an allotetraploid of the Shasta holly fern and *Polystichum lonchitis* (L.) Roth, the mountain holly fern, a widespread fern that is similar to the western sword fern but smaller and that typically occurs at higher elevations than western sword fern. The allotetraploids have twice as many chromosomes as the diploids; they also have larger spores. Allopolyploid species often have larger spores (or pollen grains, in the case of flowering plants) than their diploid progenitors. Figure 5.15 shows the evolutionary origins of these two allotetraploid species.

CONCLUSION

We have reached the end of our story. We started with rare individual mutations in populations of plants. Most of these are ephemeral, destined to die out after one or a few generations, but the same mutations may occur repeatedly over time. A few increase in frequency so that populations become polymorphic for two or more genetic forms. Some of these polymorphisms, such as leaf chevrons in clover, are perpetuated for thousands or millions of years. Some mutations replace the original form in certain populations or in some geographical areas, resulting in the genetic divergence of populations and eventually the evolution of new species.

Hybridization and genetic changes in chromosome numbers can also result in new, genetically distinct species. These new species now have separate evolutionary destinies of their own, mutations will occur in them, polymorphisms may become established in them, and they may diverge again. Genetic variation is a fundamental characteristic of all life and is the source of new life forms. Populations and species of

APPENDIX

PLACES TO LOOK FOR GENETIC VARIATION IN PLANTS

Jericho Park, Vancouver Several examples discussed in this book can be seen in Jericho Park. At the far west end of the park we have seen pink-flowered yarrow (probably escaped garden plants) growing with white-flowered yarrow. They are in flower from late spring through summer. White-flowered mutants of chicory are fairly common on the slopes south of the ponds. Lupines (*Lupinus polyphyllus* Lindl.) are common here too, so you might search for flower-color mutants in them in summer. Polymorphisms for leaf chevrons in red and white clover can be seen all year, and red and gold salmonberries can be seen in summer. Tristylous purple loosestrife occurs at the west end of the ponds and in low areas west of them. Loosestrife flowers in late summer and some-times into early fall.

University Endowment Lands, Vancouver Poly-morphisms for leaf chevrons in red and white clover are common along the edges of the woods. We found a white-flowered red clover mutant here along Marine Drive. In summer there are red and gold salmonberries everywhere. Patches of foxgloves that are polymorphic for hairy stems and flower color are common in clearings and along roadsides. The flowers can be observed in summer, and the hairy stems from spring through fall. Pink- and white-flowered dame's rocket can be found in some disturbed areas—along Imperial

Drive, for example. We found the orange-fruited mutant of red elderberry on the Endowment Lands a few summers ago. Presumably it is still there.

Dioecious species to watch for include willows and osoberry, which flower in April. Osoberry is rather rare but does occur on slopes west of the parking lot overlooking the beach where NW Marine Drive starts up the hill west of Spanish Banks. It also occurs on the cliff tops along SW Marine Drive. In summer dioecious white campion can be found in disturbed, weedy areas, and dioecious wild blackberry is common in the woods.

University of British Columbia Botanical Garden, Vancouver The native plant garden in the UBC Botanical Garden contains a good collection of mutants, polymorphisms, and hybrids of British Columbia plants collected from around the province. Among the mutants growing there are variegated-leaf forms of false box, red flowering currant, and black cottonwood; leaf-form mutants of red alder and several maples and conifers; gold-spot dogwood; white-flowered red flowering currant and fireweed; double-flowered salmonberry and thimbleberry; and many others.

Polymorphisms cultivated at the garden include farewell-to-spring with spotted and unspotted petals and sea blush with winged and wingless fruits. Various cultivated varieties of shrubby cinquefoil, as well as wild plants, are also displayed.

Hybrids of red and yellow columbine, red and white campion, and manzanita and kinnikinnick are cultivated with the parental species. Summer is the best time to see these, although some examples are observable in spring and fall as well. Red and gold salmonberries occur throughout the native garden, and clover chevrons can be observed in the weedy areas around the parking lot.

Cypress Bowl Distylous deer cabbage is common along the trails in the swampy places west of the parking area. It flowers in midsummer at this elevation.

Hollyburn Ridge Distylous deer cabbage occurs in wet areas and around the lakes on the ridge, and distylous bogbean is found in a few ponds here. Both flower in summer at this elevation.

Centennial Park, Ladner Tristylous purple loosestrife flowers here in late summer and early fall.

Redwood Park, Surrey We found populations of dove's foot cranesbill here that were polymorphic for pink and white flowers.

Howe Sound to Whistler Ponds and lakes in this area have distylous bogbean growing along the edges or even on floating mats of sphagnum moss. Bogbean usually flowers in June in this area.

Mt. Seymour Park Hybrids between the two subspecies of foamflower, *Tiarella trifoliata* ssp. *trifoliata* and ssp. *unifoliata,* are found here in the forest at about 1000 m altitude.

Washington Park, Anacortes, Washington This lovely natural park near the ferry terminal in Anacortes has outstanding displays of native wildflowers in early spring. They are at their best from April to early June. Pink sea blush is common; look for flower-color variation and polymorphic fruits. We once found a mutant sea blush here that had no flowers, just small leaflike structures where the flowers should have been. Because the plant could not reproduce, that mutation was doomed to extinction. Yellow monkey flower in Washington Park is polymorphic for leaf spots; the highest frequency of spotted plants is right above the high-tide line. These plants are best observed before they flower or at least early in the year, in March and April. Blue-eyed Mary is common, and flower-color variation can be seen. We have not found plants with spotted leaves here, however. The beautiful deer head orchid or calypso, *Calypso bulbosa* (L.) Oakes, is polymorphic for flower color here. The normal color is a beautiful orchid pink, but a large number of plants here have flesh-colored flowers. They bloom from mid-April to mid-May.

Mill Hill Park, Victoria

The parks around Victoria are ideal places to look for variation in wildflowers in spring. At Mill Hill we have found white-flowered blue-eyed Marys; you might look for pink ones or other variations in flower color as well. Sea blush is common here, and you can see flower-color variants and fruit polymorphisms.

Large- and small-flowered yellow monkey flowers and the little monkey flower, *Mimulus alsinoides* Dougl., occur here. Look for variation in the mahogany-colored spots on the flowers. Yellow monkey flower usually has lots of small spots, and little monkey flower usually has one big spot per flower. Plants with no spots on the flowers at all or with the spot pattern of the other species can also be found, however. The two species do not hybridize but appear to mimic each other. This interesting phenomenon has not yet been studied. Also look for polymorphisms in calyx spots and other variation in these variable plants.

Camas is common here; keep an eye out for white-flowered mutants. We found our twisted green-flowered mutant shooting star here. Farewell-to-spring polymorphic for petal spots occurs in the park. Hybrids between manzanita and kinnikinnick have also been seen on Mill Hill.

Thetis Lake Park, Victoria

Sea blush, blue-eyed Mary, yellow monkey flower and little monkey flower, and camas are common here and show the same kinds of variation found at Mill Hill. Watch for white-flowered mutants of grass-widows, which bloom early, in March or April. Most of these species can also be seen in Francis Park, Mt. Douglas Park, and any other area with rocky hillsides where oaks and arbutus grow.

Cathedral Grove, Macmillan Park, near Port Alberni

We found one white-flowered salmonberry bush here; it still exists and flowers in April and early May. This is a good place to see foamflower populations polymorphic for the *trifoliata* and *laciniata* leaf types. The plants are all along the trails.

Elk Falls Provincial Park, Campbell River   We have seen pink-flowered blue-eyed Mary growing here and sea blush with fruit polymorphisms.

Beach parks from Nanaimo to Campbell River These parks are good places to observe the leaf-spot polymorphism in blue-eyed Mary in early spring or even during the winter. Rathtrevor Beach Park, near Parksville, and Miracle Beach Park have polymorphic populations. Yellow monkey flower occurs in most of these parks as well and may be polymorphic for leaf spots, calyx spots, or general anthocyanin pigment in the plants.

GLOSSARY

agamospermy The asexual production of seeds, without fertilization of the egg. The seeds and plants are genetically identical to their female parent.

allele One of two or more forms of a gene.

allopatric speciation Gradual evolution of a new species by genetic changes in some populations that are geographically isolated from the rest of the ancestor species.

allopolyploid A polyploid originating by the addition of unlike chromosome sets, usually following hybridization between two different species.

allotetraploid An allopolyploid with four chromosome sets.

anthocyanin A group of plant pigments, usually red or purple or blue, that are water soluble and change color depending on the acidity of the solution in which they are dissolved. They usually occur in the vacuoles of plant cells.

assortative mating The situation in which similar individuals are more likely to mate than individuals that are unalike in some character.

biosynthetic pathway A series of chemical reactions in a cell by which one substance is changed into another. The reactions are controlled by enzymes; each enzyme is produced by a specific gene.

breed true To produce one phenotype upon selfing or crossing.

cell wall The more or less rigid box surrounding all plant cells. It is made of cellulose fibers and other substances secreted by the living cell.

chimera An organism composed of two or more genetically different tissues.

chloroplast A discrete body or organelle inside plant cells where photosynthesis occurs.

chromosome A structure consisting of a linear sequence of genes on a DNA molecule, combined with proteins and other substances. Chromosomes occur in the nucleus of a cell, and, in a simpler form, in chloroplasts and mitochondria.

cline Gradual change in a character or characters in populations of a species over a geographical range.

clone A group of genetically identical individuals derived by asexual reproduction of a single individual.

codominance The situation in which a heterozygote shows the phenotypic effects of both alleles. The heterozygote is usually intermediate between the phenotypes of the two homozygotes.

continuous variation Variation among individuals in which all intermediate stages can be seen and the differences cannot be divided into discrete groups.

cytoplasm All of a cell except the wall, nucleus, and the solution in the vacuole; all of the "living" parts of a cell except the nucleus.

development The process of growth and structural change from the fertilization of the egg to the death of the individual.

dicots Colloquial term for dicotyledons, one of the two major evolutionary groups of flowering plants. They are usually characterized by two cotyledons or seed leaves in the seed and on their seedlings, by a distinctive internal anatomy, by flowers with many parts or parts in multiples of four or five, and by broad, net-veined leaves.

dimorphism The existence of two distinct forms in some character in the individuals in a population.

dioecious plants Plants in which some individuals produce flowers with pistils but not stamens and other individuals have stamens but not pistils. Plants with pistils, which develop into fruits with seeds, are analogous to females. Plants with stamens, which produce pollen, are analogous to males.

diploid An individual, or cell, having two chromosome sets.

disassortative mating The situation in which mating between individuals that are unalike in some character is more likely than mating between similar individuals.

discontinuous variation Variation in which the individuals can easily be divided into discrete forms.

diverge To become different genetically.

dominant allele An allele (e.g., A) that expresses its phenotype in both the heterozygous (Aa) and the homozygous (AA) condition.

ecotype Populations of a species that are genetically different and in which the genetic differences are adapted to a specific habitat or environment. Different ecotypes can interbreed and merge with each other where the environments are intermediate.

enzyme A protein that controls or regulates a chemical reaction in a cell. Each enzyme is produced by a specific gene.

frequency-dependent selection Natural selection in which the rare gene or phenotype has an advantage over the common one.

form Generally, any distinguishable variant. Taxonomically, a rare, sporadic genetic variant in a population that is conspicuously different.

gene The fundamental physical unit of heredity, a section of a DNA molecule that codes for some specific function or molecule in an organism.

gene pair The two copies of a particular type of gene present in a diploid cell, one in each chromosome set at a corresponding position on the chromosomes.

genetic drift Random changes in the frequency of an allele (gene) in a population.

genetics The study of (or the laws of) inheritance in living organisms.

gynodioecy The situation in which populations of an organism consist of hermaphroditic individuals (producing both pollen and seeds) and separate female individuals (producing seeds but no pollen).

habit The characteristic form and lifestyle of an individual, organism, or species.

habitat heterogeneity A term used to indicate that even a small area occupied by a single population contains many different habitats.

hermaphrodite An individual with both male and female sex organs. In flowering plants, an individual that produces both pistils and stamens, or a flower with both pistils and stamens.

heterogametic sex The sex that is heterozygous for sex chromosomes or sex-determining alleles and hence produces two different kinds of gametes with respect to the sex chromosomes or genes.

heterostyly   A floral polymorphism in which the two or three different forms produce flowers that differ reciprocally in pistil and stamen length.

heterozygote   An individual having different alleles of a gene in its two chromosome sets (e.g., *Aa*).

heterozygote advantage   The situation in which the heterozygote is at a selective advantage over the homozygotes for both alleles.

homogametic sex   The sex that is homozygous for sex chromosomes or sex-determining alleles.

homostyly   The condition in which an individual plant or species produces flowers with pistils and stamens of the same length and has been evolutionarily derived from a heterostylous plant.

homozygote   An individual having the same alleles of a gene in its two chromosome sets (e.g., *AA* or *aa*).

hybrid   The offspring of a cross involving parents of different genotypes. Often the term is used to indicate the offspring of a cross between different populations or species.

hybrid swarm   A population containing individuals of two different species, hybrids between them, and F_2 generation recombinant individuals and individuals resulting from crosses between the hybrids and one or both parents.

inbreeding depression   The phenomenon in which offspring from self-fertilizations or matings between relatives are less vigorous or less fit because they are homozygous for recessive deleterious alleles inherited from their heterozygous parents.

incomplete dominance   The situation in which a heterozygote shows a phenotype quantitatively intermediate between the two homozygous phenotypes.

jumping gene   A fanciful term to describe the pieces of DNA that are known to be able to move from place to place in the chromosome set. When the jumping gene lands in the middle of another gene it can inactivate that gene. Function can be restored if the jumping gene leaves the inactivated gene.

meiosis   Two successive nuclear divisions, with corresponding cell divisions, that produce sexual spores (or gametes in animals) having one-half the chromosomes of the original cell (one set instead of two chromosome sets).

meristem   A region of a plant, such as the tips of roots and stems, where new cells are produced by cell division.

microhabitats   Small areas with different environments within the area occupied by a population.

mitochondria   Discrete bodies or organelles within cells where large amounts of chemical energy are produced to do the work of the cell.

molecular genetics   The study of the molecular structure of genes and their function.

monocots   Colloquial term for the monocotyledons, one of the two major evolutionary groups of flowering plants. They are characterized by one cotyledon or seed leaf in the seed and on the seedling, by a distinctive internal anatomy, by flowers with parts usually in threes or multiples of three, and by narrow, parallel-veined leaves.

monoecious plants   Plants in which all individuals produce some flowers with pistils but no stamens and some flowers with stamens but no pistils; the individual flowers do not have both pistils and stamens.

monomorphism   The situation in which only one form of a character or gene occurs in a population.

morph A discrete form or state of a particular character, as part of a polymorphism.

mutant An organism or cell carrying a mutation.

mutation An inheritable change in a gene. The term is applied both to the process of change and to the resulting new gene.

mutator A gene that stimulates other genes to mutate.

negative assortative mating See *disassortative mating*.

nucleus The relatively large, membrane-bound body or organelle in a cell that contains the chromosomes.

pin The form of a heterostylous plant that produces flowers with long styles or pistils and short stamens.

polygenes A collection of genes, each with a small additive effect, that all act to control the phenotype of a character that shows continuous rather than discrete variation.

polymorphism The existence of two or more distinct forms in some character in the individuals of a population.

ramet An individual of a clone.

recessive allele An allele (e.g., *a*) whose phenotype is not expressed in a heterozygote (*Aa*).

self-incompatibility The condition in which fertilization and seed production do not occur in a plant pollinated with its own pollen because the sperm is physiologically prevented from reaching the egg.

selfing Self-fertilization.

shade leaves An environmentally induced modification of leaves that grow under conditions of low light intensity. They are usually larger and thinner and may be darker green than normal leaves.

species   A kind of organism. Species are populations that are genetically similar and at least potentially capable of mating with each other. They are genetically different from other species and do not interbreed or hybridize with other species in nature, or, if they do, they do not do it often enough to lose their own genetic distinctiveness.

stable polymorphism   A polymorphism that persists indefinitely in a population.

subspecies   Populations of a species with a distinctive geographical range that are genetically different but fully capable of interbreeding with other subspecies of the species and intergrade with other subspecies where their ranges meet. They are not usually as different genetically as are different species, but sometimes the distinction is rather arbitrary.

sun leaves   An environmentally induced modification of leaves that grow in bright light. They are usually smaller, thicker, and a lighter shade of green than normal leaves.

sympatric speciation   The formation or evolution of a new species within a population of the ancestral species.

thrum   The form of a heterostylous plant that produces flowers with long stamens and short styles or pistils.

transient polymorphism   A polymorphism in which one of the forms in the population is in the process of being replaced by another.

transmission genetics   The study of the mechanisms involved in the passage of a gene from one generation to the next.

vacuole A membrane-bound fluid-filled sack in a cell.

variety The same thing as a subspecies. Often but incorrectly used to mean a cultivated variety.

SUGGESTED READINGS

Briggs, D., and Walters, S.M. *Plant Variation and Evolution.* New York: McGraw-Hill, 1969.
A short pocket book with many illustrations, some of which are in color. Technical, but quite readable. Examples are drawn mainly from European plants, but many have been introduced in British Columbia. Although this book is out of print, it is available through libraries.

Clark, L.J. *Wildflowers of the Pacific Northwest.* Sidney, B.C.: Gray Publishing Company, 1976.
A large coffee-table book lavishly illustrated with splendid color plates and containing a wealth of interesting information about the species covered. Less showy species are not included. This book is often useful in plant identification.

Hitchcock, C.L., and Cronquist, A. *Flora of the Pacific Northwest.* Seattle: University of Washington Press, 1973.
The standard flora of the Pacific Northwest. By working through the keys, you will be able to identify any plant growing in the area. Most species are illustrated by attractive line drawings. Contains a lot of information on polymorphisms, forms, varieties, and subspecies. Indispensable for the serious student of plants in nature.

Handbook Series, British Columbia Provincial Museum, Victoria.
This series contains many books that are useful for plant identification. Those focusing on plant families are the

most relevant. These handbooks can be quite technical, but they are inexpensive, well-written, and well-illustrated.

Hosie, R.C. *Native Trees of Canada.* Don Mills, Ont.: Fitzhenry and Whiteside, 1979.
A comprehensive survey of trees showing distribution maps and illustrated with many black and white photographs.

Kruckeberg, A.R. *Gardening with Native Plants of the Pacific Northwest.* Seattle: University of Washington Press, 1982.
An illustrated guide to growing native plants.

Larrison, E.J.; Patrick, G.W.; Baker, W.H.; and Yaich, J.A. *Washington Wildflowers.* Seattle: Seattle Audubon Society, 1974.
A paperback with keys to conspicuous flowers and many photographs, both color and black and white.

Lyons, C.P. *Trees, Shrubs and Flowers to Know in British Columbia.* Vancouver: J.M. Dent and Sons, 1974.
Lyons, C.P. *Trees, Shrubs and Flowers to Know in Washington.* Vancouver: J.M. Dent and Sons, 1974.
Small inexpensive pocket books suitable for taking into the field. Illustrated with line drawings of a folksy but appealing nature. A good introduction to plant identification.

Suzuki, D.T.; Griffiths, A.J.F.; and Lewontin, R.C. *An Introduction to Genetic Analysis.* San Francisco: W.H. Freeman and Company, 1981.
A standard text on genetics written for university students. Useful in answering specific questions on various aspects of genetics. Illustrated with many line drawings and black and white photographs.

INDEX

211

queen cup, 68, 69

ramet, 62
ratios
    9:4:3, 40
    3:1, 26, 27, 88
recessive gene, 4
red alder, 72, 75, 140, 196
red campion, 180-82
red elderberry, 58-59, 196, Plate 10
red flowering currant, 51, 81, 196, Plate 8
red huckleberry, 16, 18
Ribes sanguineum. See red flowering
    currant
root hairs, 9
Rosa nutkana. See Nootka rose
Rubus chamaemorus. See cloudberry
Rubus discolor. See blackberry, Himalaya
Rubus laciniata. See blackberry, evergreen
Rubus parviflorus. See thimbleberry
Rubus spectabilis. See salmonberry
Rubus ursinus. See blackberry, wild

Salix. See willow
salmonberry, 195, 198
    double-flowered, 61-62, Plate 14
    with red and gold fruits, 137-38,
        Plate 27
    white-flowered, 42
Sambucus racemosa. See red elderberry
saskatoonberry, 175
sea blush, 19, 21, 179, 197, 198, 199
    flowers of, 136
    height of, 12-13
    petal color of, 13
    variegated, 81, 87
    white-flowered, 46
    fruits of, 1, 2, 130-37
sectors, 16, 31
Sedum spathulifolium. See stonecrop
self-incompatibility, 30, 153, 154
self-pollination, 22, 24
Senecio cymbalarioides ssp. *moresbiensis.*
    See Moresby butterweed
Senecio vulgaris. See groundsel
sepal, 24
sex cells, 23
sex chromosomes, 141
sex genes, 143
shade leaves, 15
shooting star, 59-60, 198, Plates 11 and 12
shrubby cinquefoil, 56-58, 196, Plate 9
Silene alba. See white campion
Silene dioica. See red campion
Sisyrinchium douglasii. See grass-widows
Sitka columbine, 182, 183
Sitka spruce, 89
species, 176
spiraea, hybridization of, 186, Plates 33,

34, and 35
Spiraea betulifolia subspecies *lucida,* 186
Spiraea douglasii, 173-74, 186
Spiraea pyramidata, 186
stamens, 61, 147
stigma, 24
stomates, 105
stonecrop, 15, 109, Plate 18
subspecies, 167
sun leaves, 15
sword ferns, 191-93
sympatric speciation, 176

temperature effects, 94
thimbleberry, 63, 64, 196, Plate 15
thrum form, 153-161
Thuja plicata. See western red cedar
Tiarella trifoliata. See foamflower
Tolmiea menziesii. See piggyback plant
topographic barriers, 167
tricot, 19, 21
Trifolium pratense. See clover, red
Trifolium repens. See clover, white
Trifolium tridentatum. See clover, annual
trillium, 64, 65, 72, 73
Trillium ovatum. See trillium
tristyly, 153, 160, 162
Triticale, 189
true breeding, 22

Vaccinium parvifolium. See red
    huckleberry
vacuole, 3, 4
valerian
    northern, 151-52
    Sitka, 151-52
    Scouler's, 151-52
Valeriana dioica. See valerian, northern
Valeriana scouleri. See valerian, Scouler's
Valeriana sitchensis. See valerian, Sitka
variegation, 16, 32, 81-87
varieties, 167, 175
vipers bugloss, 45
virus, 15, 16

water birch, 74, 76
western red cedar, 72, 74
white campion, 141, 143-45, 180-82
willow, 149, 196
witches'-broom, 15, 17

X chromosome, 141, 145

yarrow, 52, 166, 195
Y chromosome, 141, 145
yellow columbine, 182-84
yew, 140

Zigadenus venenosus, See death camas

214

PICTURE CREDITS

Color Plates 4 and 5 are by Dr. Helen Kennedy; all the others are by the authors. Plates 9 and 22 appeared previously in *Genetic Analysis: A Set of Slides to Illustrate Genetic Principles* by A.J.F. Griffiths (San Francisco: W.H. Freeman and Company, 1981) and are reproduced here with permission.

Figures 1.1, 1.16, 1.17, 2.7, 3.1, 3.13, and 4.4 appeared previously in *An Introduction to Genetic Analysis*, 2nd ed., by D.T. Suzuki, A.J.F. Griffiths, and R.C. Lewontin (San Francisco: W.H. Freeman and Company, 1981) and are reproduced here with permission.

Figures 1.11, 1.13b, 1.14, 1.16, 1.17, 1.19, 1.20, 2.7, 2.9, 2.13, 2.16, 2.18, 2.19, 2.20, 2.22, 2.28, 2.29, 2.34, 2.35, 2.38, 2.39, 2.40a, 2.42, 3.1, 3.2, 3.3, 3.4, 3.6, 3.7, 3.9, 3.10, 3.14, 3.17, 3.23, 3.24, 3.30, 3.31, 3.32, 3.34, 4.3, 4.4, 4.6, 4.11, 5.1, 5.4, 5.6, 5.7, and 5.11 are by A.J.F. Griffiths.

Figures 2.1 and 2.8 are by Dr. Helen Kennedy.

Figure 2.3 is taken from a color slide by Terry MacIntosh.

Figures 2.21, 3.28, and 5.9b are reprinted with permission from *Davidsonia,* the journal of the University of British Columbia Botanical Garden.

Figure 2.24 is taken from a color slide by Dr. Roy Taylor.

Figures 3.5 and 3.13 are provided by Dr. W. Ellis Davies.

All the remaining figures are by Lesley Bohm.